THE**PRINTED**
PERFORMANCE

D1614742

RESEARCH GROUP FOR ARTISTS PUBLICATIONS

Edited by Martin Rogers and Simon Cutts

THE PRINTED
PERFORMANCE

BRIAN LANE Works 1966–99

ISBN 0 9540639 0 2

Copyright © 2001 Research Group for Artists
Publications and the contributors.
Designed by Colin Sackett.
Printed by Russell Press, Nottingham.

Distributed for Coracle and RGAP by
Cornerhouse Publications
70 Oxford Street, Manchester M1 5NH
tel 0161 200 1503
fax 0161 200 1504
email publications@cornerhouse.org

Research Group for Artists Publications
School of Art and Design, University of Derby,
Britannia Mill, Mackworth Road,
Derby DE22 3BL

CONTENTS

JOHN BEVIS

FROM FLUXUS TO FORENSIC SCIENCE BY WAY OF THE NORTH POLE

One of the guiding instincts in Brian Lane's life was his love of ritual. Ritual of all sorts—from witchcraft to all-in wrestling, from festival traditions to the recondite arts of letterpress printing. The simple pleasure in the observance of orderliness; the thrill of fulfilled expectations; the balmy membership of some historic continuum kept alive though the use of ritual vocabularies and customs; all contribute to the ceremonial discipline of the will, as the agenda of numerous religious movements testifies. Through ritual, civilizing behaviour. What better way to put up the shutters to chaos?

BL sidestepped the problem inherent in ritual, a tendency to become stale or pompous, by the judicious application of wit. An example is the 1978 publication *Some Improbable Openings*. This parody of the chess-technique manual offers, without text or explanation, eight different game-plans, in which the logic of the chess game is forsaken. Instead we enjoy the incongruous possibilities of the chess-pieces laid out with a batty but cheerful symmetry. It might be seen as a subversion of the constraints to the interplay between, on the one hand, the ritual of standard moves and, on the other, the drama of the strategic, as prescribed by the rules of the game; or perhaps an essay in how to be absurd without being merely anarchic.

Like any true lover of ritual, BL created his own. *Quiet Yellow Sounds on the River / Red with Menace* records a one-off ritual intended 'toward an understanding of the graphic images created by uniform objects floated on the surface of moving water, through the medium of an activity on the river at Great Blakenham, Suffolk.' The activity, which took place on 3 May 1975, was the setting adrift of a number of 'red and yellow spheres'—painted polystyrene balls— which were collected from some point downstream where they washed up on the river bank. The ritual was completed by the publication of a boxed edition containing one each of the coloured balls, 'the edition dictated by the numbers of relics recovered'. This was not the first, or last, time BL dallied with the problem of imposing an urban sensibility on an uncompromisingly rural setting; here a lightness of touch, allowing the event to literally take its own course, ensures that in this model the red and the yellow are in with an equal chance.

This occurs at a point which BL occupied for some time in the late sixties and early seventies, at the confluence of performance and publishing. It might be contended that in some ways BL remained true to that interplay, with the literal theatricality of performance art giving way to a more subtle kind of performance, the adoption—and adaptation—of existing literary and graphic formats. In this thesis we see BL's later career of, principally, a writer, as a ritual celebration of diverse literary conventions. As a true crime writer, he would metaphorically—and sometimes literally—wear a deerstalker and cape; but he always retained that professional freedom as a quick-change artist to don one of the many other costumes in his figurative wardrobe. He could, at the drop of a hat, perform with equal aptitude as artist, proof reader, archivist, designer, entrepreneur, or any other one of a score or more roles. A one-man band, his stage was the compositor's bench, the Reading Room, the magistrates court.

(BL's 'costume drama', by the way, deserves a chapter to itself. He never merely dressed up. Like the best of actors BL became the part so convincingly that he persuaded his audience that a latent Victorianism (the historic period of choice) had somehow been awoken in him, in his surroundings, even in the audience themselves, from a state of suspended animation, alive and well but out of sync by a time-lag of a hundred-odd years. The present became imbued with the past: to share a taxi with him was to be aware that only a fluke separated this from a ride in a hansom cab, clattering over the cobbles through the murk of a London pea-souper, hard on the trail of probity. Or so it sometimes seemed.)

During his performance-art period in the late sixties BL's work came under the Fluxus umbrella. One of the tools which was so characteristically Fluxus as to seem, in retrospect, a Fluxus cliché, was the issuing of deadpan instructions to do silly things: 'Tear this page into small pieces and scatter into the central fan'; 'Stick the labels onto any object you choose and it will become a fully authorized FLUXmasterpiece'. BL adopted not only this convention, but also the self-subverting philosophy behind it; in the words of founder George Brecht, 'Fluxus encompasses opposites. Consider opposing it, supporting it, ignoring it, changing your mind.' BL's response, in one of the leaflets for the 1968 'Rainbow and The Fluxus Leaflet Concert', took a swipe at both the rigid imperatives of bureaucracy (a popular target at that time) and their ironic insinuation into Fluxus hyperbole: "This is a Fluxus Concert ... Obey All Instructions. Obey Them Immediately"; a wry hint at the fun that might be had from an art movement which delighted in juggling, contorting and exploding the conventions of its own making.

About this time BL wrote a text entitled *Garnet*, extracts of which were quoted on the handout produced for his funeral. The style of this was quite different, a tract of cosmic discovery which might have invited comparisons with *Jonathan Livingstone Seagull*, say, or the *Siddhartha* of Herman Hesse. Very much a piece of its time, with its 'hundreds of swifts sailing overhead and close, teaching David to fly the air like them on beautiful crescent wings', it was one of BL's rare forays into the world of fiction. Once again BL succeeds in capturing the literary tone of the zeitgeist: that swooping flow through consciousness which picks up and carries with it whatever may be encountered, whose path is a serendipitous journey from the zen of one moment to the next along a string of spontaneous observations, finds a neat metaphor in the bug-gleaning flight of the swift: 'At the end of the lake the waters are ringed with unreal and transparent mountains in the midst of the lake and in the late afternoon the sun is a dull ball through the clouds which cover the sky with strange patterns...'. *Garnet* has charm and wonder in plenty, but that Utopian mannerism thwarts the instinct for hawkishness and cunning, the Brian Lane who is at his best ruffling the feathers of his pragmatism at some more rugged target. Why *Garnet* remained unpublished is interesting: perhaps because BL was, exceptionally, a stern critic of his own work, he passed his own judgement of this as a desk-bound script; or, perhaps, because there was a hint too much yearning, too much of the 'looking forwards and backwards from where we stand in this our journey' for one so clandestine about some surprisingly ordinary particulars of his own life. At any rate, he does not appear to have made further attempts at the genre.

In the mid-1980s BL created a new dramatic image for himself. As a true crime writer, he delighted in the ritual of standard literary styles, which he used straight or else filtered through his own exuberant wit to arrive at an original kind of parody. His range was comprehensive. He could write with a concise and didactic precision, as for example *The Encyclopedia of Forensic Science*, where in the Introduction he sets out his stall: 'Books on the subject have tended to fall into two main types—textbooks for the scientifically educated and trained [...] and those popular compilations of anecdote and story sprinkled with a heavy scientific seasoning lifted from the textbooks. What was required was a serious attempt to demystify for an informed readership of crime enthusiasts [...] I have relied on a hundred and one sources and the patience of very many people in order to grasp the fundamentals of processes and instrumentation, both scientific and intuitive. *In short, if I could understand it, there was a good chance my readers could.*' [My italics] The style, then, was that of popular non-fiction, such as the Pelican, Newnes and Collins 'Readers' of the mid-twentieth century, and that the book succeeds triumphantly is testament to BL's diligence as a researcher, to his ability to explain complex issues with clarity and insight, and to his skill at pitching the tone and style straight to the square leg of the beguiled amateur.

On the other hand he was quite adept at the populist, thriller style of journalese. There was a deliberate nod in 'The Murder Club' publications towards a market which would look for entertainment and titillation, the chuckle over a little carnal swagger, as for example: "On 17 August 1983, Douglas Crabbe was refused a drink in the bar of the Ayers Rock motel; the staff thought he had had enough. As if to prove them right, Crabbe left the bar, climbed into his articulated truck, and drove it through the motel. He killed four people instantly and seriously injured twelve more ..." There is in this something of the slick and amoral style essential to pulp fiction; full marks, though, for expediency.

The other side of this same coin is the sermonizing morality of the tabloids— BL treasured such front-page banner headlines as the "Rot in Jail You Bastard" with which *The Star* greeted the conviction of Ronald Barton for the murder of his step-daughter Keighley in 1986. This was a style BL co-opted for some of the cases made more sensitive by the involvement of children, the use of extreme brutality, or the topicality of popular outrage. He tended to maintain his own professional impartiality in such cases by quoting from the polarities of opinion, and indeed like many another true crime writer, never missed an opportunity to quote from different sources, such as coroner's reports and witness statements, to enable a richer mix of styles on the page.

In particular he was fascinated by the literary efforts of some of those remembered—if at all—for more infamous activities. One example was a "rambling, disjointed and sometimes incomprehensible" murder story, written by Gunner Reginald Buckfield when he was remanded in 1942 for the murder of Ellen Symes at Strood, in Kent. The writer's intention was to reveal an alibi, but unfortunately the story contained information which only the killer would have had. A brief extract will suffice to give a flavour of the 'style': "I made tracks out of the pub just at 8.10pm, reached another called the *Ship Inn* at 8.30 or 8.35pm, stopped till 8.50 to 8.55pm, made tracks towards Dillywood, got settled down after all these little things were done by me at 10.15pm ..." and so, on and on. BL saved this text from justified obscurity by publishing it for the first time in *The Murder Club Guide to South East England*, and in so doing put yet another voice on stage—the vernacular of the semi-literate man who 'thinks he has a book in him'. But the story carried an additional fascination for BL: in writing this apparently harmless piece of fiction, Reginald Buckfield was to all intents and purposes signing away his own liberty. At his trial Buckfield was found to be guilty but insane, and spent the remainder of his life in Broadmoor.

There are a number of similar instances in the *Murder Club Guides*, BL's original foray into the world of true crime writing, such as a the reproduction of a play (or 'melo drama') on the case of Abraham Thornton, a short story by the writer and murderer Percy Mapleton, essays on the subject by Dickens, de Quincey and Thackeray, articles on the murdered playwright Joe Orton, and reproductions of paintings with murderous connections by, among others, Walter Sickert and the fantasy-artist, father-killer and madman Richard Dadd. There is no doubt some pragmatic reason why these and other cases were not collected into a single volume, but surely the greatest book Brian Lane never wrote would have been titled *The Fine Art of Murder*, or, perhaps, *The Artist Murderer*.

Among these 'artistic' reproductions were a number of broadsheets—'penny dreadfuls'—issued to commemorate the discovery of a crime, arrest and trial of a suspect, or most particularly public execution. They were typically composed at short notice and run off in print runs of a million or more for the most notorious crimes. Here another voice is heard—that of the hack writer of the shoddy, unimaginative doggerel of the 'Lamentation' of the condemned prisoner:

> I am a maiden in youth and bloom
> I a wretched murderer to die am doom'd
> And in the city of Salisbury
> My days must end on a dismal tree.

Dismal indeed. An occasional venture entered into by BL was the manufacture of facsimiles of these, as well as ballad broadsheets and Wild West posters, using photocopies which were treated to the aging processes of folding, creasing and soaking with tea. They were never intended to be mistaken for the original, but were a parody of another kind. What was being appropriated here was not the original endeavour, but rather the historical gap between the original and the facsimile. The naivety, the ghoulishness, the clumsiness of these ephemeral tracts thrown together in a matter of hours becomes something else when they are so self-consciously printed with the patina of the intervening years.

An acknowledgement of this habit of appropriation comes most explicitly in the form of the 'Fog Log Collection'. The second in the series, *Fridtjof Nansen's Fog Log*, culls fourteen extracts from the July–September 1893 period of the Norwegian's account of his first Arctic expedition, each recording the prevalence and describing the effect of fog. Nansen wrote these by hand in the log of the

Fram, and the line-by-line account of day after day of nothing to see becomes an introspection, a focusing-in on Nansen's vision. Subsequent to the voyage the handwritten script went through the processes of being edited, typeset and printed. Eighty years or so later, Brian Lane was to copy extracts from the published book, *The Farthest North*, line by line, in his own handwriting, as Nansen had done originally, concluding with the duplication of the explorer's signature.

The delicate slightness of the final publication, the sense of it as a wafer of pure intensive labour, the corollary between the ceaseless movement of the pen across the page with the impetus of the expedition, the recourse to one more convention—the allegory—in which Man, Ship, Ice and Fog are the key players, make this perhaps one of BL's most sophisticated and successful projects. He leads us to discover as much integrity in the unflinching regularity of his own handwriting as if it had been that of Fridtjof Nansen himself. It is the perfect appropriation: by writing the words as if they were his own BL gets inside his model, becomes the author. Not the author of the expedition, but the author of those strange, eerie times when the ship was alone in the fog, adrift among the icebergs, when there was nothing to see and everything to listen out for.

MICHAEL LUMB

LUMB**LANE**

Last week, I received a letter from the artist, John Upton, in response to my request for help with my research on Ray Johnson, Pop Artist and 'father' of mailart. John wrote, "I might be wrong but Suzi Gablik told me that the only people she knew he (Johnson) was writing to in Britain in 1966 was an art gallery called 'Gallery 10' (sic) at Blackheath. I have stuff sent by them, but never met them." I wrote straight back to John Upton and he sent me photocopies of two postcard-works sent by Brian Lane, one dated November 1966 and the other January 1967. The first is probably the earliest extant Lane printed work. Coincidentally, it was in either late 1966 or early 1967 that I met Brian Lane. The formalised partnership, Lumb Lane, however, did not come into being until the mid 1970s.

My first awareness of Brian was through an advertisement that he had placed in a journal asking for people to contact him if they were interested in being involved in an avant-garde arts festival, which he had proposed for Greenwich. I was then living down the road from Blackheath and arranged to meet Brian in his gallery. My overriding memory of this first visit was of his collection of printed matter on pigs. I was aware of an extraordinary level of thoroughness in the documentation of this material, a thoroughness that I was to see as a major part of his working methods and was to grow to admire immensely. The festival did not take place but Brian and I discovered that, although neither of us had trained in Fine Art, we shared a passion for experimental work. Whilst Brian had trained as a printer, I had trained in theatre design and was a set designer working for the B.B.C. Brian talked about his performance proposals and I, mine.

Later, Brian set-up rehearsal space at Oval House. Around that time, 'Pavilions in the Parks' were launched which were temporary structures on the Chelsea Embankment, which were made available to artists. Brian put both my name and his own forward as wanting to use one. I went to see the names taken out of a hat. There, Brian introduced me to the woman who accompanied him as 'Rainbow Day'. Brian had adopted the performance persona, 'Rainbow Day, Brian Lane and the First Dream Machine'. This 'name' came about as result of a typing error—the omission of the word 'the', preceding 'Rainbow', prompting Brian to decide that rather than staging an intended, 'Rainbow Day', he should acquire a person named Rainbow. Rainbow's true identity was kept secret and to this day nobody connected with the performances knows who she was.

Brian's name was not pulled out of the hat, but mine was. On discovering the small size of the pavilions, I realised that it would be totally impossible for me to perform my intended works in the pavilion if there was to be an audience. In typical radical fashion, Brian recommended omitting the audience. Later, in a Lumb Lane interview with Freda Constable for Radio Orwell, Brian declared, "It is more important for us ... than it is to present it to other people ... it is ... very anti-social." I never really shared this opinion and I gave the pavilion to Brian. Sadly, although one of Brian's business cards of 1968 includes my name, I was obliged, for personal reasons, to withdraw from working with the group that Brian had set-up, before the first performance.

Brian made his last performance in 1970 and set-up his imprint, Probable Latitude 76° 15' Longitude 113° 10'E, almost entirely to publish the work of other artists. He also set-up a graphic design company, Black Circus Designs, for economical reasons and in 1973/4 worked in Geneva for the second time as a proof-reader and copy-preparer for the International Telecommunications Union (previously he had worked for the United Nations). On his return, Brian took a job with the Science Museum. Meanwhile, in 1968 I moved to working with London Weekend Television, lost touch with Brian and in 1971 left LWT to move to Suffolk and start-up an arts centre near Ipswich; the Arts Workshop at Henley.

In November 1974 Brian and I met-up again. Throughout the intervening period Brian had remained involved in printing and I had continued to make Fine Art works, but soon things were to take-on a different momentum for both of us. In 1974 I made my last painting and began making installations. As Brian believed profoundly that painting was 'dead', my rejection of painting was a point in my favour with him. Brian described our joint situation in our unpublished catalogue of 1977, "...where once their work had been complementary, it was now parallel. Both were discovering the relevance of objects and situations placed within the real space and real time of natural landscape—Lumb notably with the installation of transparent, semi-transparent and mirror substances, Lane in the effects of camouflage. This led during May and June 1975, to three major works of collaboration." It was clear to both of us that we could benefit enormously from each other's support.

My rural home in Henley, near Ipswich, provided an ideal opportunity for the realisation of a number of Brian's projected works. The first of these was *Against the Landscape*, a major, year-long work created for a specific landscape in Suffolk. Brian variously referred to this work as an event, a survey and also as a sculpture, all of which terms allude to different aspects of this complex process-piece work. Begun in May 1976, it was in two parts, described by Brian as, "A sculpture on the land of Suffolk conceived by Brian Lane and built, erected and recorded In collaboration with Annetta Crane, Michael & Janet Lumb." For Brian, having worked with a group of people on his earlier performances, it was entirely natural for him to include others in identifying creators of a piece of lan-dart. This work consisted of "A series of clusters of banners, camouflaged against a stretch of 100 metres of Suffolk hedgerow", and two rows of ten miniature bell tents, camouflaged to the grass. This piece demonstrates Brian's interest in aspects of military life during wars, which was to be revisited in a number of subsequent, printed works.

Essential and central to the work is the photographic recording of the process of change during the year, in both the landscape and the imposed flags and tents. These photographs were taken from "static viewpoints" at the same time on the first Monday in every month. Brian was concerned about the possibility of the loss of documentation, through fire or some other mishap and so two copies were made of all photographs, one kept by Brian, and the other by me. For Brian, documentation was not only essential during the work but also through-out the preparation leading up to the piece itself. Central to the documentation produced for this work, is a typed list of 'documents', itemising 49 elements, including dated letters between the two of us. A typed 'programme', states the exacting work to be carried-out: whilst the tents were to remain for the entire year, one flag had to be removed from each of the clusters, on the first Monday of every month, "...if necessary, shaken clean and dried. It is then placed in a black, clean polythene bag and sealed". As well as the monthly tasks, there was also a daily weather report, recorded on a printed form.

Documentation for Brian also took the form of what might be considered to be contextualisation, a printed A4 sheet, as a flier for the event, with quotations about flags in wartime and photographs of soldiers with a ragged flag and a pho-tograph of bell tents. Two other similar reproductions complete the documenta-tion. His programme of 20 March 1975 concludes the final paragraph with, "This ends the survey and the rest of May 1976 to be spent cataloguing the documen-tation with view to an exhibition. Design of 'Relics' publication." Whilst a printed work of the tents was eventually published, no other relic appeared and Brian lost belief in the value of exhibitions for his work. This attention to documenta-tion was the standard by which Brian worked in all his Lumb Lane works.

Whilst the work in the landscape continued, Brian carried-out another work, *Quiet Yellow Sounds on the River / Red with Menace* which he credited to the same three people as *Against the Landscape*. Brian described the intention of the work on the flier as being, "Towards an understanding of the graphic images created by uniform objects floated on the surface of moving water, through the medium of an activity on the river at Great Blakenham, Suffolk." This was a work, described by Brian as a 'situation', with approximately 150 red and 150 yellow small polystyrene balls released from a bridge onto the river and eventually retrieved by the people who had come to witness the event. Brian and I made a photographic record of the patterns made by the balls on the river, in black and white and on colour slides. The work led, in 1978, to the production of relics. These are Rexene covered card boxes, containing one each of the retrieved yellow and red balls, with a colour photograph and printed text. "The edition is dictated by the number of relics recovered, and is approximately 150. In addition, an especially bound box has been produced in an edition of 10."

The third "major work" that Brian referred to in the catalogue was my installation, *The Chimerical Hexagonal Void*. Like Brian's works, this was realised in collaboration, not only with Brian, but also with members of the Arts Workshop. The work utilised the architectural features of the exhibition centre in Ipswich Town Hall, continuing my then current theme of working with translucent materials, obscuring and changing vision. The work was ritualised in its construction and photographically documented at each stage, producing a photographic relic, which so far remains in an edition of one.

These three works were followed in 1976 by a number of installations that I created for the landscape. The first, *The Strontium White Winter Canes*, a three dimensional model of the Strontium Emission Spectrum, scaled to three feet lengths of bamboo, was erected in a wood at Skeets Green, Suffolk. The proposal was to record the work in each season but this aspect of the work was not realised due to the work being stolen within a short time of its installation. The subsequent, *Where Any Angled Light Would Congregate Endlessly* was a much more ambitious work, and again, one of collaboration. Poet, Nick Clay wrote a site-specific poem in 100 parts, be they phrases, words, or parts of words. The text was Letrasetted onto the inside of polythene bags that were then sealed. The entire work of 100 bags was suspended by cotton from the trees at dawn, on the first day of spring 1976, by a number of members of the Arts Workshop and of course Brian. The work was photographed on colour slides and black & white—what had become standard procedure for our works, however, this work was also filmed. As with *The Strontium White Winter Canes*, It had been intended to record it at each change of season, anticipating that by autumn, the letters would have begun to fall-off, thereby making new sense of the poem.

In the event, the 100 bags, placed in the same wood as the previous work were systematically removed. Subsequent publicity revealed that this, unlike the theft of the previous work was a deliberate act of sabotage by unknown members of the public who believed that the work should not have been placed there. Whilst it was clearly a disaster from the point of view of the work, Lumb Lane soon realised that the resultant correspondence in the *East Anglian Daily Times* could be encouraged to continue into a polemic about art. This was helped enormously by a member of the Arts Workshop taking a trip to Belgium and writing from there as well as Brian, writing from Geneva, to which he had once again been called. Eventually, the newspaper declared the debate terminated. This unanticipated 'artwork' in the form of the letters, demonstrates an interest that Brian and I shared in both polemic and found works.

Lumb Lane produced one further landwork. Brian had made a proposal for a printed work entitled *Earth Displacement*, which consists of nine drawings on A6 record cards of (im)possible earthworks. Although this was never published, in 1978, he published two other sets of drawings from 1975, *Circular Displacement* and *Linear Displacement*. It may be that Brian had realised that it was not important for him to carryout the 'proposals', feeling that it was sufficient for the reader to imagine what the works would look like. In December 1975, Brian produced a further proposal, entitled *Earth Displacement for Michael and Patsy*, based on squaring the circle. This earthwork, on my land, was carried-out in 1977, entirely by Brian and me, the Arts Workshop having folded. The work was the removal of a cylinder of earth that was then placed in the form of a cube, a visual realisation of the concept of 'squaring the circle'. Although this was executed, the documentation was not carried-out as planned, namely to record it until it eventually returned through slippage, into the original hole. It was clear that Brian was moving on to new things and that carrying-out this proposal was no longer of interest to him. This was to be the last work that Brian was to make in the landscape and the last non-printed work on which we collaborated. From this time Brian worked solely with printed and small private works.

In 1976, Simon Cutts acquired a property in Camberwell High Road, a few doors from Brian's flat in Wyndham Road, which was to become Coracle Press and gallery. Brian had known Simon Cutts from Gallery Number Ten days and immediately threw himself wholeheartedly into the preparation of the gallery space as well as taking on the role of technical adviser to 'Coracle Press'. No doubt this gave Brian a thirst for producing printed works again, something he had hardly, if at all, done in the previous five years. Brian and I began discussing printed works, usually prompted by found printed material, although it was to be some years before any of them were realised.

Before Brian went to Geneva, he and I adopted the 'flag', 'Lumb Lane'. I suspect that it was Brian who observed that there was a street in Bradford, in the notorious red-light district, called 'Lumb Lane' and this would be a suitable name under which we could work jointly. A friend of mine who was an amateur photographer, Cliff Hoppitt, was scheduled to travel to Bradford and undertook to take a photograph of a Lumb Lane street sign. We adopted this photograph as, in effect, our signature. The intention was never to work jointly in the conception and execution of works in the way that Gilbert and George have, but as Brian wrote in the catalogue, "Lumb Lane provided a certain anchor and common source of experience—not least preventing the otherwise inevitable duplication of effort." For me it also provided a sympathetic sounding board as well as giving an added, social, dimension to the carrying-out of projects.

In 1976, Brian and I exhibited in the Industrial Sponsors Exhibition at Hugh Mackay and Co. Ltd. London. Our exhibit took the form of a slide show of our collaborative works to date. We then planned an exhibition for late June for the same space in Ipswich that I had used for my installation. The geographical distance caused by Brian being in Geneva between 1976 and 1978, his third contract abroad, again for the International Telecommunications Union did not prevent this show happening and following organisation by letter and telephone, Brian returned to Suffolk for the exhibition that took place from June 28th to July 9th. The show was entitled *In the earliest days*, an 'exhibition of statements and ongoing works'. It was divided into three sections, Completed works, works in progress and works that Brian in a Lumb Lane interview with Freda Constable, prior to the show, described as, "possibly the most important, works that could and should be carried through to the end." In this, Brian was referring to works at the proposal stage.

Whilst it was clearly useful for us to see the work displayed and pleasant to share it with the guests we were acutely aware of the limitations of the exercise in terms of the numbers with whom we were communicating as well as opportunities for further showings. The exhibition had broken with the tradition of showing finished work and given the number of statements and proposals included, had a distinctly textual flavour, not least with Brian's extensive documentation for *Against the Landscape*.

Brian was profoundly dissatisfied with the exhibition, in part I suspect, because he had lost interest and faith in the gallery system as a whole. He wrote in the catalogue, "In retrospect, the exhibition was neither useful nor stimulating." Whilst this is typical of Brian's invective, it was clarified by the following sentence, "Its feedback was nil ..." It was apparent that the necessarily large amount of textual material in the exhibition made total absorption an unattractive proposition, given that it was all wall mounted. It was therefore, not such an enormous step for Brian to have proposed that we make no further attempts to exhibit the existing, or any future work, but instead produce a Lumb Lane catalogue to distribute around the world, no doubt, using Brian's contacts made through the International Mail Art Network. This scheme would allow the comfortable reading of the works and inevitably produce feedback and probably open-up interesting international opportunities for further work sites.

In April 1977, Brian produced 'regulations' for the "Style and presentation of Lumb Lane material." This deals with standardisation of recording such things as measurements, with proposals for a bank account and with "credits" which were to be 'Lumb Lane', clearly indicating how seriously Brian was still taking the Lumb Lane partnership at that time.

Despite Brian living in Geneva, we began work on the major publication of our works, collected together as Lumb Lane. The catalogue covered the period April 1975 to October 1977. Brian wrote in the introduction, "Work has been selected to show one (or both) of two things:

a) a considered general significance in the framework of a larger body of international art.

b) an indication of the development of Lumb Lane over this period—given a diversity of concerns."

The catalogue was divided into four sections, following the sections of the exhibition. In fact it could be said that the catalogue was largely the exhibition expanded and, redesigned into book format. Section One, "works within the period which have been completed." Section Two, "works which for a greater or less period of time, are continuing towards the realisation of a primary concept." Section Three, contained proposals and the last section, entitled "Editions" covered printed works. The finished manuscript contains 45 pages at A4 size.

The 'completed works' section (One) begins with our three 'major works' as well as my earlier and later land-installations. The letters that formed the debate around *Where Any Angled Light*, in the *East Anglian Daily Times* were also included as a work in their own right. Whilst in Suffolk, I continued to make land-based works Brian, in Geneva, produced a number of city-based works that he included in this section of the catalogue. *Small Flags in Geneva* consists of single objects mounted on A6 index cards, collected by Brian and Debbie Squires, (Brian's, partner at the time) whilst walking from opposite ends of the street. *Due North of Geneva* consists of photographs taken facing due north of Geneva at the point at which Brian and Debbie met in each street, whilst carrying-out *Small Flags*. Both works are collated in alphabetical order of street name. *Rue Francois Ruchon* records, "...the tangible features of a street and its accessibility to essential services and shops." Brian and Debbie's flat overlooked the street. The finished work consists of a set of 24 A4 photocopies. Whilst these three works are still outdoor works, *When We Heard the News* took on very different subject matter. This consists of about 100 index cards each with a photobooth photograph of Brian and Debbie, taken when they had heard the news for that day. The record cards have handwritten text on them and Brian asserts that, "The ... photos ... were never determined by the news items of the day." This latter piece was conceived by Brian as a wall piece, evidenced by his photograph of a mock-up in his flat. Structurally, the blocks of photobooth photographs follow a horizontal line, with mounted cuttings from the press placed above and below the photobooth portraits for the relevant day.

Two other works by Brian appear in Section One of the Lumb Lane catalogue. *Portrait of Bruce Nauman*, is not a documentation work, and unlike the above Geneva works is attributed by Brian to Lumb Lane, although I had no part in it. The work became somewhat of an obsession with Brian as it appears in five different editioned variations, produced between 1977 and 1978. In each case, the work consists of a nameplate 'Bruce Nauman' placed on a fountain in rue de la Corraterie, Geneva. The work makes a play on Nauman's *Portrait of the artist as a fountain*. This could be said to fall into the category of Brian's 'observations', notes on the absurdities of life. *Gary Gilmore Fan Club, Bumper Pack* however is an altogether blacker obsession and foretells Brian's later preoccupation with murder that was to become his source of income as a writer. This is an astralux wallet containing a membership card with plastic wallet, T-shirt transfer for hot iron, large badge, pencil and a postcard inviting the purchaser of the work to become a member of the fan club. For Brian, the work spoke of the heroising of gangsters, "gangster-as-hero" and presumably prompted Brian's later money spinning idea of forming the subscription 'Murder Club'.

Whilst documentation was essential to Brian's land-based works, documentation in itself was overtly the primary interest of the Geneva works. As with *Against the Landscape*, these works required printed forms on which to record and document the work. I too had moved to works that were primarily about documentation. In 1974, I had conceived the idea of collecting and documenting the placement of found pieces of string that had knots in them. *String Collection* required similar documentation to *Against the Landscape*, as did two other works of mine, *Great Buildings of the World* and *Great Squares of the World*. Buildings,—a celebration of the family snapshot which requested a close-up photograph of a companion against a non-descript wall of the 'great building' and *Squares* required a photograph of pigeons on the ground in the great square. In the case of all three works, it was open to anyone to participate and send me the relevant photographs with the completed form. Brian not only printed the forms for these, but also participated in each of these works that were included in Section Two.

Two works in the section of ongoing works (Two) represent Brian. *Faded Flower Water*, which was precisely what it eventually was, a labelled set of 17 very small test tubes with rubber stoppers, containing water which was documented on labels. Brian's comment on the work in the catalogue, "Inspired by Leopold Bloom's sentiments on the subject in James Joyce's 'Ulysses'", indicates his considerable eclectic knowledge and source of references. It seems that he probably had ideas of further works involving stained water. *In Good Company* consists of a series of index cards, each documenting Brian with another person, be they someone he knew personally, such as me, or a cartoon character in a street fair such as 'Barbapapa'. This work was also documented and recorded on a form. Two photographs recorded each encounter, one *In Good Company—Brian Lane* (with another person) and the other, *In Good Company* (Brian) with the other person. Again, Brian comments in the catalogue, "I have noticed a lot of name-dropping and such among artists recently. I am decided to be photographed only in good company".

Land Transference, another work of mine, represented in this section, recorded, over a period of one year, the absorption of a foreign piece of land by surrounding flora. "The transference of an equal cubic capacity of land from Lumb to Lane and Lane to Lumb, Suffolk to London and London to Suffolk", was eventually carried-out, in 1980, between France and Suffolk, with another person, Brian having moved-on to other things.

Section Three, 'proposals' consists of only three works, one by Brian and two by me. Brian's proposal was for a performance of works by Robert Bozzi, George Brecht, Alan Brett, John Cage, Brian Lane, George Maciunas, Cavan McCarthy, Thomas Schmit, Mieko Shiomi, Hugh Shrapnel, Ben Vautier and Lamonte Young. Fluxus artists as well as people that Brian had published at Gallery Number Ten are heavily represented in this list—Brian had performed the Fluxclinic in Aberystwyth in November 1968. Two quotations accompany the proposal for this work, Samuel Beckett's, "It is all very well to keep silence, but one has also to remember the kind of silence one keeps" and the second, a quotation from Edmond and Jules de Goncort, "Gautier exclaimed '... I am just like you, I prefer silence to music'". Brian not only used these quotations but also letrasetted them with a view to making them into some kind of printed works, part of his interest in statements as an end in themselves. The concert was never realised and as far as I know, Brian made no attempt to realise it. I am represented by my proposal from 1968 for a series of performances collected together as the *Darkness Concert*. This was the concert that I had hoped to perform in the Pavilions in the Park. However, it has still not, to date, been performed. The final work in this section is a proposal of mine for 'Rainbow Balloons for Ay-O'. This was for the photographic recording of model tissue paper hot air balloons, one of each colour of the rainbow to be released into the sky in the order of the rainbow.

The final section was of editioned work, whether already printed or proposed, although the catalogue does not specify which. Whilst there are works that we each produced and/or proposed independently, there was also a body of work that we produced together. Independently, there is a 1972 land-based leparello of mine—a proposed land-referenced work that was never realised; my *Chimerical Hexagonal Void* documentation works as well as two bookworks from what became the *Henley Project*; three books satirising aspects of the nature of contemporary art and two little handmade works exploring my interest in transparent substances.

Brian included his documentation of *Quiet Yellow Sounds on the River / Red with Menace* and *Against the Landscape*, the former eventually produced and published in 1978 as described above. *Against the Landscape* is described in the catalogue as "An edition of recovered tents consisting of one unused (dyed to match the ground) and one after one year." As I have said, Brian moved on to focussing on printed works and this section includes a number of his works that were eventually printed in 1978 as *Information Series One*. This was a series of A6 format postcards and wallet based works where he felt that the images and/or text given were sufficient in themselves; they were his sharing of his own observations. Number Ten in the series is *The Land Tents*, folded card with before and after black and white photographs of the tent installation. Brian included two other works, Number Three—*Granatelli in Town* and Number Nine—*Airships (Shadows)*. In both cases these are the result of armchair excursions, which is to say that the works were inspired by other printed matter. *Granatelli* was inspired by photographs of the car magnate found in an automobile magazine—a subject that Brian to my knowledge had no interest in. This is perhaps the most difficult of Brian's printed works, as it contains no clue at all as to what the work demonstrates. For Brian, the fascination was the series of photographs of a very overweight businessman, presumably it is the visual appearance that we are invited to engage with. *Airships (Shadows)* is bubblegum card photographs, in an A6 astralux wallet, of the shadows of airships over a desert.

The communal works epitomised Lumb Lane's way of working in that Brian and I were amused by the sometimes-ludicrous relationship of images to text. This was epitomised in a treasured book of mine, *The Vegetable Garden Displayed* (I was at the time, a keen gardener). A number of postcard works were proposed, inspired by this book. A triptych, *Soft fruit*, which pointed to the puzzling similarity between three photographs showing fruit canes being planted, blackcurrants, whitecurrants and redcurrants, all indistinguishable from each other. *Firming the ground by treading*, a similar work showing a man walking on soil, with the captions, 'onions', 'planting cabbages', 'seed-bed for raising plants' and 'seed bed and seed sowing'—again, the images are indistinguishable in reference to their titles. Eventually I printed these works as postcards and Brian used a further image, a spade, placed at the end of a trench with the caption as the title, *How to dig*. This appears as *Information Series One, Number Six*, a single fold of card and also as a postcard, *How to dig (1)*, which is included in *Selection of five postcards from Information Series One—Set One*. Brian used one further image from this book, *The Asparagus Patch*, printed as *Information Series One, Number Five*. In this single fold of card, he again looked to military matters by placing a photograph of a vegetable asparagus patch next to an 'asparagus' tank trap.

Although none of Brian's printed works listed in the catalogue had been produced at the time, Brian made other printed works in Geneva in 1976. These were in editions of five or six and no doubt he saw them as being private, lyrical works that he preferred to give to one or two close friends rather than print in large editions. He was at this time making works with Debbie Squires (*Small Flags*) and, removed from his archive in London, he may well have been more inclined to produce a number of much lighter works.

An undated (pre-1977), typed A4 sheet describes Brian's proposal for *Information Series Four*. "The first direct collaboration of Lumb Lane and a joint extension of Brian Lane's continuous sequence of 'Information Series'. One sheet will be issued each month serving partly as a vehicle of communication presenting aspects of work in progress and partly for the presentation of observations and independent 'information'. Information Series Four is available on subscription at £4.50 per year (12 issues) post paid. These first three sheets have been sent out free." This unrealised proposal describes Brian's interest in and ambition for the *Information Series*.

By the time the final artwork had been produced for the catalogue Brian had lost interest in all but printed work. This is where his newfound relationship with Coracle Press and his training could be exploited to the full. It might well have been his realisation that this is where his interests had shifted to that led to him blocking the printing and publishing of the catalogue. Brian would have known from his work with mailart around 1966 that there are many opportunities for distribution of printed works through the post, without the benefit of a large Lumb Lane catalogue.

This was to signal the end of the Lumb Lane collaboration, although we continued to exchange printed works through the post and, on my visits to London, Brian was an invaluable source of advice for me on the production of further printed works. One or two joint proposals were worked on, such as a book on Photoart and 'The Artist Publisher' but none of them came to fruition, although in 1986, a much-shortened version of 'The Artist Publisher' formed the basis of the Crafts Council exhibition of the same name. Brian included my books in the exhibition, as well as making reference to Lumb Lane. "This disenchantment (with the exhibition) led to the production of the Catalogue as an alternative to 'exhibition', and though in this form it still has shortcomings, it does provide an improvement: ... In book form the material presented is capable of reaching a far larger group of spectators and prospective patrons than would a single exhibition for a specified period in a static location ... The intimidation by time often detracts from the work in a gallery, while book form allows the absorption of concepts free from temporal/locational pressures .... (from a joint statement by Michael Lumb and Brian Lane. 1976)". This was to be the final appearance of Lumb Lane.

ADRIAN GLEW

DR FLUXUS

Brian Lane was among a handful of people in Britain, who was aware of, and corresponded with, Fluxus artists during the 1960s. Indeed, he took on board some of their precepts and presented Fluxus scores during an intense period of performance activity from 1968–70. Remnants of these Fluxus events, as well as related material, reside in Lane's papers, which are now housed in the Tate Archive (TGA 2000/3). The archives were generously donated by the artist's mother, through the assistance of many of Lane's friends, in the Spring of 2000. The papers help to form a picture of Brian Lane's involvement with this under-ground group of artists at this crucial period of its development.

As many will know, Fluxus was a radical collective of international artists who collaborated in Europe, the USA and Japan during the 1960s and 70s. Primarily centred around George Maciunas, Fluxus emerged out of post-war artistic changes, fusing elements of Futurism, Dada, Russian Constructivism, the Bauhaus, Marcel Duchamp and John Cage. The group's work was intentionally ephemeral and deliberately by-passed the gallery and museum system through performance, films and publishing. George Maciunas, who had conceived of Fluxus as an alternative direction to the commodity oriented high culture preva-lent during the period, described the movement's intentions in a mid-1960s manifesto: "Fluxus art-amusement is the rear guard without any pretention or urge to participate in the competition of 'one-upmanship' with the avant-garde. It strives for the mono-structural and non-theatrical qualities of simple natural event, a game or a gag. It is the fusions of Spike Jones, Vaudeville, gag, children's games and Duchamp".

Before the arrival of Lane's papers into the Tate Archive, the key manifesta-tions of Fluxus activity in the UK were generally recognised to be 'The Festival of Misfits' of 1962 and the 'Fluxshoe' touring exhibition of 1972–73.

The 'Festival of Misfits' was a labyrinthine exhibition at Gallery One in London from the 23rd October to the 8th November 1962. It was organised by the gallery's founder and director, Victor Musgrave and the 'nouveau realiste', Daniel Spoerri, who was given the task of selecting the participants and shaping the Festival. In addition to Spoerri himself, the Festival eventually included:

Robert Filliou; Dick Higgins; Alison Knowles; Arthur Kopcke; Gustav Metzger; Robin Page; Emmett Williams; and Ben Vautier. The gallery was soon transformed into a tactile maze by Spoerri and his collaborators. Within this labyrinth, Filliou created 2 spinning poetry wheels which instructed visitors to perform simple actions; Gustav Metzger hung copies of the *Daily Mirror* reporting the Cuban Missile Crisis; Robin Page constructed a sound environment made out of everyday objects; Emmett Williams attached numerous rubber stamps to a wall for visitors to create poems, while Ben Vautier lived in the gallery window for 15 days and nights, labelling everything as a work of art and offering himself for sale as a 'living sculpture' for £250. Press interest in the Festival was intense and the 'exhibition' and concert became a benchmark for Fluxus activity in the United Kingdom.

The 'Fluxshoe' of 1972–73 was organised by David Mayor a research student at the University of Exeter. He had meetings with and wrote to many of the Fluxus personalities. Mayor appears to have been most influenced by George Brecht's definition of Fluxus as involving "individuals with something unnameable in common". Thus, 'Fluxshoe' became a platform for performances and events by people with similar attitudes whether they were allied to 'official' Fluxus or not. By the time 'Fluxshoe' opened in Falmouth, over 100 Fluxus and non-Fluxus artists had agreed to appear in one guise or another, i.e. either in person or represented in some way in the exhibition or catalogue. The tour encompassed seven venues in all, including: Falmouth (23–31 Oct 1972), Exeter (13 Nov–2 Dec 1972), Croydon (15–26 Jan 1973), Oxford (10–25 Feb 1973), Nottingham (6–19 Jun 1973), Blackburn (6–21 Jul 1973) and Hastings (17–24 Aug 1973). In total, there were nine Fluxus artists who attended at least one of the 'Fluxshoe' venues, including Eric Andersen, Ay-O, Davi det Hompson, Alice Hutchins, Per Kirkeby, Taskehisa Kosugi, Carla Liss, Knud Pedersen, and Takako Saito. Overseas and British artists who appeared in person included: Ian Breakwell, Stuart Brisley, Paul Brown, Helen Chadwick, Marc Chaimowicz, Henri Chopin, Robin Crozier, Allen Fisher, John Gosling, Mary Harding, Anthony McCall, Opal L. Nations, Genesis P-Orridge and Cosey Fanni Tutti, John Plant, Carolee Schneemann, Endre Tot, and Paul Woodrow.

Although, the 'Festival of Misfits' and 'Fluxshoe' were the major manifestations of Fluxus in the U.K. during this period, there were also other important Flux-related activities. These and non-Fluxus events added to the melange of avant-garde activity that permeated the country during the 1960s and early 1970s of which Brian Lane was an important figure. One of the earliest of these manifestations was Gustav Metzger's series of Auto-Destructive demonstrations, exhibitions and manifestos of 4 Nov 1959, 10 March 1960 and 23 Jun–3 Jul 1961. Metzger's events culminated in the 'Destruction in Art Symposium' held at the I.C.A., around London and in Edinburgh, from 31 Aug to 30 Sep 1966. The I.C.A. and its Bulletins were an important source for the display of, and debate about, the avant-garde throughout this period. Though not held at the I.C.A., 'The Little Festival of New Music', on 6 July 1963, at Goldsmith's College (University of London), was—after the Festival of Misfits—the most significant Fluxus event. The Festival included pieces by John Cage, Cornelius Cardew, George Maciunas, La Monte Young, George Brecht, Robert Watts, Emmett Williams, John Cale, Nam June Paik, Tomas Schmit, and Robin Page. A number of Fluxus artists were regular visitors to, and exhibitors in, Britain, notably Yoko Ono ('Unfinished Paintings and Objects', Indica Gallery, Nov 1966 and the 'Half-a-Wind Show', the Lisson Gallery, Oct–Nov 1967); Robert Filliou ('Machine Poets', I.C.A., 28 Mar 1963 and his trip to Leeds in June 1969 where he created an eponymous card game); and George Brecht and Robin Page who lived and worked in Leeds (Page creating a Christmas event on 25 Dec 1966 where he lay naked to receive gifts sent to him by, among others, Mieko Shiomi, Daniel Spoerri, Robert Filliou, Eric Andersen, Wolf Vostell, and Hans Sohm).

Up until now, Lane has seemed a peripheral figure in British Fluxus with the occasional mention in Maciunas's famous Fluxmail lists and in the odd issue of the Fluxus periodical *V TRE*. It is only after consulting Lane's papers in a more systematic way that one can see the scale and level of his dissemination of the Fluxus creed. As early as 1967, it seems Lane presented a Fluxus concert at Gallery Ten in Blackheath under the auspices of his own Project 67. And in a later letter to John Osborne, he refers to forming, at this time, a London 'branch' of the Fluxus group commenting, "we have had made available to us many of the scripts and scores written such infamous 'Happenings' [sic] men as Ben Vautier, Allan Kaprow, George Brecht, Ay-O, Chieko [later Mieko] Shiomi, Lee Heflin, Jean-Jacques Lebel and Milan Knizak". He also indicates that they built into the live programme "much experimental music under advice from Jeff Nutbeem and Tom Phillips". It seems probable, from the extent of material in the archives, that Fluxus editions and publications were available for purchase from the gallery at this time. Lane was also in contact with the young Fluxus artist, Ken Friedman evidenced by a review, of one of Lane's Gallery Ten boxes, by Oswell Blakeston which appeared in *What's On in London* for 22 September 1967. Here Blakeston mentions among others, Friedman's poem on a long paper strip, curled like a Christmas cracker snake in a cardboard ring.

On 15 November 1968 the very first Fluxclinic was 'performed' by Lane,

Maureen Sandoe and others at Oval House, London. This was a participatory work originally created by the Japanese group, Hi Red Center, and first performed at the Waldorf Astoria Hotel, New York City on 4 June 1966. The Fluxclinic includes a specially printed form, the *Record of Feats and Features*, where measurements such as maximum hair length, capacity of mouth and contents of handbag or left pocket were recorded for each participant. Lane prepared a whole series of instructions detailing how the Fluxclinic should be performed. For instance, in his *General Note on Fluxclinic equipment and procedure*, he notes:

> All examiners should have white hospital coats on, preferably
> printed with 'Fluxclinic'. ...
> It is preferable to have a mains water supply and drainage.
> Otherwise more buckets will be needed..
> A general supply of clean cloths and kitchen paper should be made
> available as many of the examinations cause mess.
> If a subject refuses to undertake any test the appropriate square is
> stamped REFUSAL in red. ...
> If possible skeletons, medical charts, X-ray, etc. should be around
> to give authenticity to the absurdity of the examination.

There was also a two page *Working Script for Examiners*, that included advice such as, "Volume of Head ... is taken by the subject immersing his head in a bucket of water and measuring the volume of water displaced into a bowl", and an *Equipment List* that inventoried bathing caps, yardsticks and a box of wet sand. All dimensions were to be taken in the most absurd manner possible. The length of breath was measured as the distance it took to blow out a candle on a tall yardstick. Other feats were tabulated such as paper throwing, where the participant was asked to throw a small piece of tissue paper without folding or screwing it up. If the paper floated behind the participant, a minus number was given. Knuckle and toe prints were stamped directly onto the forms, whilst the contents of handbags or pockets were listed and weighed. ESP was even tested with the examiner asking the subject whether there was a red or white ball in his left pocket. If guessed correctly the form was marked "YES", and if not "NO".

From 27–29 November 1968, Lane produced a mini festival of experimental work within the Aberystwyth Arts Festival organised by the University College of Wales, with the flyer announcing:

> International Graphic Poetry: experimental poems from all over

the world, collected by Rainbow Day, Brian Lane, and the First
Dream Machine. In the Parish Hall ALL 3 DAYS.

CAUTION: ART CORRUPTS.

On the Wednesday, there was a programme of experimental musical sounds,
including works by Stockhausen, Italian and Dutch composers. There was also
an opportunity for audience participation. Then on the Thursday, a Fluxconcert
was announced with the advice that "if you don't know what a Fluxconcert is,
you must come and see for yourself". In addition there was another outing for
the Fluxclinic, which operated throughout the three days. It appears that experimental films were to be shown (quite possibly Yoko Ono's infamous *Bottoms*
film), but the flyer states that "because of the exigencies of the forces of law,
order and repression" this had been cancelled. Finally, on the Friday, there were
to be "poetry events of all shapes and sizes to amuse, startle and explode the
mind." With entrance at three shillings for each event "A good time was guaran-
teed for all". The festival and in particular, Lane's contribution was reviewed in
The Guardian as "A State of flux at the festival" by John Hall. Hall especially
enjoyed the Fluxconcert: "Brian ... showered down leaflets of instructions. War
Game The pictures you are about to see are silent. You have been provided
with materials to make a sound track. Fluxus bids you fight well. God is on your
side."

It was during 1969 that Lane met Bill Harpe of Great Georges Project (GGP)
in Liverpool at a meeting of the Arts Council of Great Britain New Activities
Committee. As a result a series of events were undertaken and sponsored by
GGP. The first of these took place in their auditorium over the weekend of 8–10
May 1970. It was wholly devised by Lane and dedicated to "Fluxus in General
and Ken Friedman and Ben Vautier in particular". On this occasion the event was
run under the auspices of Lane's new venture, 'Probable Latitude 76° 15'
Longitude 113° 10'. There were two events, a Fluxus Leaflet Concert on May
8th: described in the flyer as:

An event in which
YOU entertain us
YOU entertain yourselves
YOU entertain each other

Printed leaflets were showered onto the audience instructing them to take
various actions to realise a series of visual and phonic poems and to make music.
Special effects made use of tape/slide/film sequences and the 'Liverpool Light

Show' provided the effects for sequences of 'poetry' and 'war games'. Then on Sunday May 10th there was another staging of the Fluxclinic using *The Guardian*'s by-line from the Aberystwyth event: "very much a Nuffield maths course, minus any educational end products."

It seems that Lane stayed on in Liverpool as he was writing, in June, to Fluxus artists, Ay-O, Mieko Shiomi, Nam June Paik, Ben Vautier and Tomas Schmit asking for ideas for the GGP summer theatre, that was to take place in the parks of the city for a period of three weeks. Specifically he wanted to have "a quantity of 'tricks' that are universally delightful". Lane hoped that they would be able to design an environment or event, which fitted in with the theme of 'magic' to be constructed or performed in an open space. Ay-O wrote back first offering his 'Tactile Wall', which suggested:

1. Make hole, any place you want
   (wall, floor or ceiling)
2. Attach material (from Ay-O's tactile list) behind hole,
   —somehow—

Later, he even sent a three-dimensional model to help Lane visualise his ideas. Shiomi also wrote back accepting the invitation to participate and promised to send plans for 'Balance Poem on the Centrifugal Land'. Whether this arrived in time for the Liverpool event is not clear, but Lane produced a facsimile script and design for this event under his Gamma Three imprint at some point during 1970. Lane also produced publications and boxes for other Fluxus artists, notably Ken Friedman and sent free copies of his *Information Series* to George Maciunas until his death in 1978.

Although, seemingly active in the Fluxus orbit for a short period of time, Lane probably made more people in the UK aware of this important laboratory of the avant-garde in the late 1960s than almost any other person; preparing the ground for others, such as David Mayor to disseminate the ideas of the collective still further. Further work still needs to be done on Lane's contribution, but from this first trawl through his archives it appears that he made an early and positive impact in Fluxus circles in Britain.

BILL HARPE

WORLDS-A-PART ?

Some projects which appear to be located worlds apart on a conventional cultural atlas may in fact turn out to be neighbours.

In the summer of 1968 the Gallery Number Ten in London's Blackheath was promoting a programme of 'Experimental Arts' with concrete poetry, electronic music, a theatre piece, and exhibitions of optical poetry and collages. At the same time Great Georges Community Cultural Project in inner-city Liverpool was initiating a programme of 'Community Arts', with artists leading play-schemes for inner-city youngsters, obstacle course games, three-legged football, and soul music discos.

Yet in 1971 the close proximity between these two enterprises was recognised when Brian Lane completed the design and printing of a multitude of varied leaflets and travelled to Liverpool from Gallery Number Ten to lead three specially commissioned events at Great Georges Community Cultural Project (soon to be known familiarly as The Blackie, the abbreviated name for the project's recently acquired home and base, a former church blackened by over a century of urban industrial grime).

The 'Leaflet Concert' was an event which might just as easily have taken place in London or New York. A variety of leaflets (with engaging, allusive, elusive, and poetic messages) together with leaflets distinguished simply by a single letter or a single word, were shared during the course of an evening with an adult audience. The audience responded by reading and discussing the leaflets, and by arranging and re-arranging the leaflets, the letters, and the words to create new messages. The audience were both receiving artworks and working (and playing) as artists themselves. But what made the event unique was the setting. For the leaflets fluttered down onto the audience below, like occasional showers of refreshing and stimulating rain, from the spacious oval balcony of the former 19th Century Congregational Church once described as "Liverpool's Third Cathedral".

The second event, 'Red Roses For Lorca' was particularly appropriate for Liverpool. The annual May Day parades were, in Liverpool of the 1970s, festive political events involving tens of thousands of participants in the most convivial of processions followed by the most convivial and uplifting of rallies. 'Red Roses For Lorca' saw the artists of the Blackie moving through the May Day procession and giving out a variety of leaflets of different colours, sizes and shapes. The leaflets, each with a quotation from Lorca, were both a tribute to Lorca and a poetic exhortation to the participants in the procession.

The third event, inspired by the work of the Fluxus Group of artists from New York, was very much a Liverpool phenomenon. Teenagers and children from inner-city Liverpool, turning up for a play and recreation session, found themselves invited to attend a 'Fluxclinic'. White coated attendants in cubicles were on hand to measure the physical attributes of the youngsters. Smiles were measured against a calibrated banana. Height was measured in chocolate bars. Weight was measured against old car tyres, chunks of metal, and pieces of wood. The 'splits' (the greatest distance each participant could put between their feet) was measured against the height of a nearby participant—giving measures such as "As far as Geraldine's nose from her toes". X-ray vision, head size, and body volume were also measured in like manners.

Each participant took away a personal record-book documenting their clinical experience (a compilation of reactions, comments, and statistics). The record-book also documented each participant's real name, age, address, and occupation—and their preferred name, age, address, and occupation. It turned out that the preferred address of almost half the youngsters of south Liverpool, the Toxteth area, was Detroit.

The 'Fluxclinic' was, like the 'Leaflet Concert' and 'Red Roses For Lorca', both a throwaway event and unforgettable. There are adult Liverpudlians, now in their middle years, who still remember and describe their 'Fluxclinic' experience. And the event itself contributed to both determining and defining the pattern of the Blackie's work with young people. The 'Fluxclinic' is described in the Blackie publication *The State of Play*, and introduced as follows, "An acquired and apparently natural fear of appearing foolish may serve as much to deprive and separate as to protect".

After these three seminal events there were no more specific collaborations between Brian Lane and the Blackie. But friendship and mutual respect, and a recognition of a commonality of cultural interests, had been established—and visits, and exchanges and correspondence continued. Packages of documentation and printed works continued to be regularly exchanged between Brian and the Blackie throughout the 1970s and 1980s, and personal contact and friendship continued through the 1990s. And Brian's continuing influence can be recognised in Blackie events to which he made no immediate practical contribution.

A few years after Brian's first visit the artists of the Blackie went out into the streets of Liverpool and set up a stall to sell poetry by weight. Weeks of preparation had gone into selecting short quotations from volumes and volumes of poetry. These quotations were then printed onto slim pieces of paper. Through-the-night sessions later resulted in these quotations being rolled and twisted into coloured cellophane sweet wrappings. Large sweet jars were then filled with hundreds of these 'sweets', and appropriately decorated and labelled (Shakespeare, Romantics, 18th/19th/20th Century, Nursery Rhymes, Family Favourites, Religious, etc).

Passers-by purchased their chosen sweets by gram-weight, and then paused in the street to open up and read their poems and to share them with friends and other passers-by.

It was an event which was serious without being solemn—humorous without being frivolous—and for-the-moment and yet unforgettable. These are also the qualities we remember and celebrate in Brian's life and work.

STEVE WHEATLEY

MURDERMAYHEM&BRIANLANE

When I first came to know Brian Lane in the mid-nineteen seventies through our mutual involvement with Coracle Press, he was a figure who was held in particular respect by all of those around him. This was not just a response to his considerable substance and experience as an artist, the list of publications he had produced over a sustained period and his enthusiastic espousal of alternative structures and venues for presenting art ideas. Brian had an unflinching commitment to the realisation of individual pieces of work which he considered of value. The support that he offered to me was crucial. He published my work through his press when I was lacking the means to take it on by myself. He helped me in a variety of ways when I was trying to establish my own publishing outlet, White Lies Publications. He also inspired and facilitated a range of one off projects, and always with the same selfless and generous creative spirit. "This is an important piece and it must be done", he would say, "I'm not telling you to do it, but you do seem to be most conveniently placed. We'd better make sure that it happens".

All of this can be said of Brian before one comes to mention what was most immediately evident on meeting him. He was a strikingly colourful character and a genuine eccentric. By temperament, he was an extremist. He maintained a set of beliefs, a moral code and a precise aesthetic sensibility, which he applied with rigour across every aspect of the life he had chosen to lead. The routines of his day, the positioning of objects and collections within his working and in his living space, the meals he prepared and ate, the drinks he favoured for particular times of the day, were all considered with scrupulous care. Everything was selected, ordered and choreographed to create a rich and distracting pattern to his day. This approach was, equally apparent in the consideration which he gave to his personal appearance. He was fully aware of his own vanity and cultivated it with some amusement. The slightly rakish beard and moustache and the deliberately rather formal choice of clothes were conceived to give him the indefinable air of a leisured Victorian gentleman. If I close my eyes and try to picture him, it is with a deerstalker, a brown suit and Ulster overcoat, a stout walking stick and a cunningly concealed hip-flask of Irish whiskey to fortify him against the country chill.

Brian was a forceful character with a magnetism which was difficult to ignore when he was in a room. It was not that he sought consciously to dominate the conversation. He was too cool for that and would indeed, have expressed contempt for such self-importance. He did, however, like to push a point to its logical end, but generally for the devil of it and with an edge of wit and detached amusement. Indeed, he had a disarming charm and a width of interest and seemingly random knowledge that was always entertaining. This was not always the way, however, when Brian was the worse for drink. He could be argumentative, awkward to a fault and at times downright rude. One would not wish to excuse this behaviour. It is, however, significant that his anger was generally provoked by disappointment with people then quickly turned to frustration and irritation. He had a horror of the mundane and the vulgar and a particular distaste for artists who fell short of the standards of commitment that he thought they should set themselves. Artists, he thought, should offer an example of total honesty and disinterested idealism. He could not bring himself to remain silent when he detected what he saw as backsliding. As a general principle he also thought it a noble aim to disconcert and undermine easy assumptions. He did not easily accept conventional thinking in either the aesthetic or the moral sphere, which he considered in any case, closely related issues. He saw it as part of his responsibility to remind fellow artists of this. Every proposition should be though through on its own merits. Laziness of thought was unacceptable and needed to be confronted. Some found this offensive and, in Brian's estimation, diminished themselves by this response. His friends were more tolerant and learnt to appreciate and respect him for it.

A desire to provoke and disrupt is also, of course, a common thread that runs through the diversity of Brian's creative output. This was generally carried off with irony and humour to seduce his audience, but was no less deliberate for that. His publications took a variety of different forms borrowed from the commercial printing world, booklets, leaflets, fliers, posters, postcards, invites, badges, found photographs, stamps, rubber stamps, whatever was recognisably everyday, easily to hand and not from the conventional art world. The material that he used to create the content for each publication was equally lifted from 'found' sources. Unconsidered and abandoned trifles discovered in second hand shops, bookstalls, libraries, or even picked up off the street or out of a wastepaper bin, were transformed by Brian's hand into a new existence where, for the first time, they were fondly perused and treasured. This became a form of social work for detritus and Brian particularly enjoyed his role as collector, editor, choreographer and mid-wife, breathing new life into old flesh. In the seventies, this was still a very real challenge to the accepted notion of the artist, though today, it is, of course, a commonplace of artistic practice. These ambitions were readily appreciated and approved of by Brian's colleagues and admirers. He was valued and applauded for both his radicalism and his endearing idiosyncrasies. There was, however, one aspect of his interests and obsessions which increasingly and at most unexpected points found its way into his work and often challenged both their loyalty and their comprehension. They could go so far in indulging Brian and his eccentricities. They simply did not get his fascination with crime and murder. It had no part in the template they had created for him as an artist. Indeed, it seemed completely out of step with the nature of his involvement in contemporary art. They were two separate worlds, which simply did not meet. The murder thing seemed to deny the very qualities that underpinned his art. It had no morality and no aesthetic. There was no idealism. It was grubby, vulgar and nasty. Brian of course, did not agree.

Brian's interest in murder, crime and punishment developed through the nineteen seventies, becoming, by degrees, an absorbing and addictive passion. He started to think in terms of specifically murder based projects, completely outside of the art arena, in the early nineteen eighties. These began to increasingly dominate his time and attention to a point where in the mid-nineteen eighties, he came to a deliberate decision to cut himself off completely from the art world. He constructed an entirely new professional life and life style for himself in the very different ambience of true-life crime writing. I knew him well and worked closely with him throughout this period, initially on art based projects, but later, in the nineteen eighties, on a number of his early crime projects. This culminated in the research and written pieces that I contributed to the early stages of his first major undertaking, which was published by Harrap Books as the eight volume *Murder Club Guides to Great Britain*, a Pevsner-esque country-wide survey of the sites of our most famous, or, should one say, infamous murders. As can be seen from the scale of this undertaking, his first published project, Brian could not be faulted for his ambition. The quantity and depth of research which was required was considerable and he was unremitting in his search for detail and accuracy.

This was, without doubt, at the root of his fascination with crime and murder. He loved the process of researching and whilst there is a wealth of available historical material, there were, at that time, few serious writers, beyond Edgar Lustgardten, Colin Wilson and Daniel Farson, who were interested in making any creative use of it. Brian was at his happiest arriving outside the old Reading Room of the British Library at nine in the morning, before the museum was open, ready to take his regular seat amongst the green leather bound desks under the great dome, with a stack of books which had been brought to him by the staff, a fresh page ready on the writing pad and his fountain pen poised for action. As his absorption deepened, he developed copious files on crime and punishment, always meticulously notated and added to as new facts were discovered from obscure sources. There were also press cuttings of contemporary cases to be constantly kept up to date. He loved this academic activity, perhaps more even than writing his own contributions to the genre. He needed to be logical, thorough and controlled to achieve his aims and this slow pace seemed to soothe his more impatient instincts. It was, at least in this sense, an unsullied activity. It had both clarity and a purity of purpose for him.

Over the long term, Brian had become increasingly disillusioned with the compromises and short cuts which seemed to be required of him to get anything done in the art field. It was too often about who you knew and being prepared to exploit opportunities that arose as much from luck and happenstance as from any principled or considered strategy. He increasingly saw a gulf between the hyperbole and the actuality of making art. It was a gap that was difficult to bridge. The whiff of hypocrisy made him uneasy. To be sure, the world of crime writing, in common with the wider world of commercial publishing, had more than its fair share of despicable motives, petty jealousies and other unbecoming behaviour, but it never pretended to be otherwise. It was unblushing in its cynicism and, in that sense it was straightforward and unpretentious.

There was one further rather obvious advantage to crime writing. It could be an occupation. If you achieved any reasonable level of acceptance, you might expect to make a living. This he did, to some degree, for almost fifteen years. Brian's work in the art field never made money, indeed, much of it was not intended for sale and was distributed free of charge through the post to anybody who expressed an interest. For a number of years he subsidised his creative work by disappearing for up to six months at a time to take up translation work in Europe. He understandably wearied of this pattern of living and, as he realised that there might be an opportunity to earn directly from something he wanted to spend his time doing anyway, he chose to take it.

This all, however, begs the question of why Brian chose murder as the particular object of his interest. A whole range of topics could have generated the research activity and some prospect of an income. His obsession with murder pre-dated by a number of years any consideration that he might have been capable of earning anything from it. The nature of his fascination was more intellectual and aesthetic in its essence. The figure of 'Doctor Death' which Brian invented as an *alter ego* for some of his publishing activity back in the seventies was loosely based on a factual character, Dr Thomas Niell Cream, who was hanged for murder in 1892. Cream was brought up in Canada where he trained as a Doctor. After a suitably disreputable medical career in America he took ship to England. Arriving in London, he proceeded to patronise a number of prostitutes in the Lambeth Road and, introducing himself as a doctor, offered them pills as a cure for various minor complaints. He performed the same service in the street on Waterloo Road. The pills contained strychnine and the unfortunate young ladies suffered a particularly unpleasant death. These crimes were not initially linked or recognised fully for what they were. Having effectively got away with it, Cream then took the extraordinary action of sending letters and having handbills printed accusing a totally innocent doctor and then a medical student of the multiple murders. By this means, Cream drew attention to himself and the crimes and was eventually tracked down and arrested.

This case had an emblematic importance for Brian. It exhibited many of the qualities that he most treasured. It was theatrical, gratuitous, and unfathomable. It had flourish, a sense of style. It remains a riddle. Why had Dr Cream committed such seemingly random, pointless and dispassionate crimes? There was no discernible motive. He expressed no particular hatred of prostitutes. Cream didn't even wish to linger long enough to witness the effects of his ghastly handiwork. Why should he make such elaborate efforts to draw attention to himself? He was an experienced trickster of evident intelligence and cunning and yet he deliberately courted arrest. He was arrogant and he was vain. He seemed to have a deep need for other people to appreciate the cleverness and elegance of his awful plans. When he was arrested and throughout the trial he showed no emotion beyond irritation at a legal process which failed to appreciate his genius. This was an appallingly perverted, disassociated man, but a perverted artist of a kind. He had style and class as a murderer.

When Brian first invited me to collaborate in one of his murder projects, he suggested that I might best understand something of the quality of his interest by reading *Murder Considered as One of the Fine Arts*, a piece written by the 19th Century essayist, Thomas De Quincey in 1825. De Quincey, who is best remembered for his essay *Confessions of an English Opium-Eater*, was an early friend of the Lakeland poets and later a prominent member of the cosmopolitan circle around Coleridge which developed a particular interest in the moral debate around various forms of socially extreme behaviour, not least murder. This was not as outrageous as it might now seem. Later in the nineteenth century murder became a common literary pre-occupation of figures as established and pre-eminent as Stendhal, Victor Hugo and Zola in France and Dickens and Thackeray in England.

De Quincey was a particularly interesting, yet ultimately frustrated figure. He had an unquenchable ambition to become a great poet, like his friends Wordsworth and Coleridge, yet his major contribution to literature was the development of the short philosophical essay, which appeared in periodical magazines and was considered paid hack work, a form which he explored and honed into an art form over a period of nearly fifty years. *Murder Considered as One of the Fine Arts* is a particularly elegant, if elaborate example of the genre. It claims, in a short introduction to be a found document for which the writer evinces moral outrage and is prepared to present to the reader only as a warning. This document, in turn, purports to be the script of a monthly lecture, the Williams Lecture, which has been presented to a fictional society, 'The Society for the Connoisseurs of Murder', based on the notorious Hell Fire Club. It should be noted at this stage that the Williams celebrated in the Lecture's title was John Williams, an itinerant sailor who committed the infamous Ratcliffe Highway murders in 1811. These murders were essentially two incidents in which whole families were slaughtered in their beds with considerable violence and gore. There was some evidence of robbery, but the crimes seemed appallingly disproportionate to this rather prosaic motive. Williams was caught, but cheated the courts and the executioner by hanging himself in his cell. His body was ceremonially paraded around the East End of London on a hurdle, pausing at the sites of each atrocity, before burial beneath a crossroads in an unmarked grave. De Quincey considered Williams to be the first authentically modern murderer, the exemplar of a new philosophical status for murder, where the actions and motives of the perpetrator can only be understood by recourse to a more psychological, symbolic and, ultimately, aesthetic reading.

The essay, itself, is both playful and deliberately provocative in tone. De Quincey proclaims, with an appropriately mock pomposity, his prerogative to write about anything he damned well pleases. He refuses to give any ground to self-styled moralists who would ascribe to him, the writer, the same opprobrium that they would apply to his subject matter, the murderer. He draws attention to the fact that one does not sanction evil merely by the action of writing about it. He is as ready as any man to offer payment to an appropriate official to apprehend any likely miscreant, but he also, by that investment, reserves the right to comment upon it. He refuses to condemn any subject out of hand as, in itself, unworthy of consideration. An object as contemptible as an ulcer may not be as pleasing to the eye as a flower or a beautiful woman, but some ulcers are more aesthetically satisfactory than others and this is worthy of remark. There may, indeed, be a perfect ulcer which the surgeon, at least, is impelled to admire for its unparalleled beauty. Such is equally the case for murder and the murderer. Moral outrage should not deny the connoisseur the right to arrive at a comparative ethical or aesthetic judgement.

Perhaps it is instructive at this point to mention the name of Doctor Hawley Harvey Crippen, a name that has become synonymous with the infamy and evil of murder. Crippen was, in fact, one of the more sympathetic characters to face the hangman's noose. He was a mild man by temperament, married for some years to Cora, a wife, who by all accounts, was an embarrassment. She was loud, vulgar and aggressive. She constantly nagged her husband, insulted and humiliated him in public, whilst expecting him to underwrite her preposterous pretensions to succeed as an actress under the name 'Belle Elmore'. She also openly carried on with a number of her actor acquaintances. Crippen maintained a precarious existence as a dentist and seller of patent medicine and, as time passed, began what seems a touchingly timid affair with his mousy secretary, Ethel Le Neve. At some point Crippen decided to poison his wife. He then cut up her body, buried it beneath the cellar of his house and took a ship for Canada with his mistress dressed up as a boy. Crippen and Le Neve were arrested as they arrived in Montreal. Throughout the trial Crippen accepted full responsibility for the crime, ensuring the acquittal of his mistress. He accepted his fate with equanimity. No one would suggest that what Crippen did was other than awful, but who could deny some sympathy for his situation or some respect for his stoicism and loyalty. He was bad, but not that bad, In fact, he had some admirable qualities.

Moving to the main body of De Quincey's text, he spends some time in laying out a typically fanciful classical history of murder. Within this framework he proposes the highly unlikely contention that most philosophers of note either have been or should have been murdered. This is a wonderfully gratuitous revenge on philosophers for the amount of time he feels he has been forced to waste by reading their endless theories.

He then arrives at his central argument. Murder of itself is not necessarily of any interest. It is the particular circumstances, which can raise it beyond the mundane brutality of a brawl. There must be some aspect of the case, the character or status of the victim or the murderer, the planning of the deed or the motive, the means employed or the disposal of the evidence, the site and locality of the murder, the date and timing of the deed, that raises it above the commonplace and the blandly practical. The aesthetics are to be found in the particular detail, the unnecessary flourish, the minor fact that sheds unexpected light, the cruel joke of chance circumstance, the satisfying symmetry of poetic justice, the potent myths that grow from prosaic events and take on a life of their own, the inexplicable mystery which can spawn a thousand theories. They can all create a kind of poetry, a genuinely aesthetic experience. If there is one murder mystery that has achieved the most enduring notoriety and has continued to generate a steady flow of literature, it is the 'Jack the Ripper' murders. What gives it this unique position is the blank canvas it presents, with just occasional signposts of evidence which are rich in inconsistency and symbolism. At the centre is the greatest conundrum of all. No one knows, or can ever know now for certain the identity of the Ripper.

As if to offer evidence of his theories of murder and, incidentally, the potency of coincidence as a poetic metaphor, De Quincey's own extended social circle provided two instances of colourful characters caught up in the most lurid of murder scandals.

William Corder, a prosperous farmer's son, continued a liaison with the daughter of one his father's tenants, Maria Marten. She conceived a child by Corder, which soon died. Corder had often promised to marry her and arranged to meet her at the Red Barn, a bleak and romantic local spot, so that they might run away together. Maria set out for the trysts dressed up as a man but was never seen again. Six months passed and Corder sent letters pretending that they were married. At this point, Maria's mother supposedly dreamt, for three nights in succession, that her daughter had been brutally slain and buried beneath the Red Barn. The earthen floor of the barn was dug up and Maria's body discovered. Corder was arrested in London, tried at Bury St Edmunds assizes and publicly hanged in August 1828, before a great crowd. Fuelled by the notoriety of the case, an extraordinary four million copies of the ballad sheet of the murder were sold and Staffordshire pottery figures and other momentos proved similarly popular. The Red Barn Murder has subsequently been transmuted into an archetype of the 'rich young rake seduces naive local maiden' myth and several melodramas and at least one film have been produced of the grizzly tale. Most gruesome of all, artefacts from the case may still be seen in the Moyses Hall Museum in Bury St Edmunds, including a record of the trial reputedly bound in Corder's skin.

Thomas Griffiths Wainewright was an equally spirited young gentleman of dubious morals. He dabbled in painting, wrote articles under the wonderful pseudonyms 'Janus Weathercock' and 'Egomet Bonmot' and exhibited evidence of a most dissolute lifestyle under the guise of these artistic pretentious. Money was a constant problem and forgery proved a useful supplement to his income. From this he moved into taking out insurance on his relatives, finding it necessary to poison, in turn, his uncle, mother-in-law, and two step sisters in order to cash in on his investments. As suspicions began to grow, he fled to Boulogne. After five years, he returned to London, thinking the rumours would have died down. He was, however, still the object of gossip, referred to as 'Wainewright the Poisoner'. He was arrested and tried, largely one suspects on account of his influential friends, on the lesser charge of his earlier efforts at forgery. Sentenced to be transported to Australia, he suggested, whilst on the convict ship, that he had, indeed, poisoned his stepsister, Miss Helen Abercromby, because he was offended by "the thickness of her ankles". Wainewright was also the subject of subsequent literature, a peon written by Oscar Wilde under the title *Pen, Pencil and Poison*.

These were the stories, the "true tales of dark deeds and arch friends" that Brian Lane really loved, with their elaborate and often slightly farcical details and an independent life which seems to grow in strength and transmute into folk lore rather than fade into the mists of time. He was rather dubious about most recent cases. It often takes time for the obscuring fog of contemporary social mores to clear, for those immediately involved to pass on and for the more interesting details of the story to gradually emerge. The libel laws have a considerable effect on any suspicions of the truth that fall short of arrestable proof. It is only relatively recently that we have learnt that Tony Mancini, who was acquitted through the clever arguments of his defence council, was without doubt guilty of the second Brighton Trunk Murder or that the police were pretty sure they knew who was responsible for the Croydon Poisonings, but could not find sufficient proof.

Brian was most at ease with the strict structures of social caste and formal manners, which characterised the Victorian era. He was fascinated by the mores of the middle classes, their prissy etiquette, their social snobbery and the deep, dark, shameful secrets which could never be revealed for fear of social disgrace and subsequent ruin. These pressures fell particularly on women, who rarely had financial independence and were reliant on marriage for security. Victorian ladies of some social position, such as Florence Maybrick, Adelaide Bartlett and Florence Bravo, were reduced to the use of poison to rid themselves of their unpleasant, unfaithful and sometimes brutal spouses. For similar reasons, Brian was drawn towards murderers with the prestige and responsibilities of a professional position to maintain. Major Herbert Rowse Armstrong, a solicitor from Hay-on-Wye, who used weedkiller he had bought for his lawn to poison his wife and make a further attempt on the life of a younger business rival, was a particular favourite. Most of all, however, he was intrigued by the doctors. There was Edward Pritchard the Glasgow doctor, who used antimony to evade the inconvenient consequences of his uncontrolled sexual appetites and Dr William Palmer, the Rugeley Poisoner, who dealt with debts he had incurred from gambling on horse racing by eliminating his creditors. There was George Lawson, who used his position as a doctor to feed his drug habit, but soon moved on to poisoning the close relatives of his wife to increase her inheritance and Buck Ruckston who strangled his wife and their nurse maid and deposited their dismembered corpses wrapped in parcels, at various points along the Carlisle to Edinburgh road. Then, of course, there was Dr Crippen and Dr Cream who have already been fully discussed.

Brian always felt that doctors were the richest source of potential murderers. Doctors not only know how to extinguish life with the maximum efficiency, they are well placed to disguise their handiwork as natural causes. No suspicion is aroused, even if they are discovered in possession of a dead body. Brian contended that many murders had slipped passed unnoticed through careful guiding hands of the medical profession. Had he lived just a little longer, Brian would have relished the full revelation of the appalling career of Dr Harold Shipman. Shipman is Brian's kind of murderer, cunning, scheming, controlled almost matter of fact about what he was doing. Yet even Brian might have been taken aback by the breathtaking scale of his activities. Murder was made an everyday occurrence. One can only suppose that Shipman exists in a cocoon of self-delusion. He would have to rationalise his actions as easing the way for his elderly patients, saving everybody involved a lot of protracted pain and bother. Given the little one has learned of what seems to be a rather bumptious and grumpy personality, however, one cannot quite believe that his motive was solely misplaced sympathy. One is more inclined to feel that it was impatience with the constant demands of the old ladies and irritation that his patients were wasting so much of his valuable time. Brian would have appreciated this appallingly mundane explanation.

One final observation might help to illuminate the drift in Brian's interest from Contemporary Art to True Life Crime writing. We have already discussed at length, Brian's appreciation of the ideas of Thomas De Quincey, but some attention should be drawn to the title of De Quincey's essay *Murder Considered as One of the Fine Arts*. There is within this form of words an implication, which De Quincey himself never quite explored. The argument has been more fully developed only recently in Colin Wilson's weighty work *A Criminal History of*

Mankind. The proposition is that the planned murder, whilst it obviously has direct destructive consequences, is nevertheless a creative act, a kind of perversion of the artist's or writer's craft. The very act of conceiving and perpetrating a murder requires the murderer to make choices about the means, the location and the timing. Any murder could, without undermining its efficacy, be carried out a whole number of different ways. The methods that the murderer settles upon, whilst being partially determined by chance, opportunity and convenience, are therefore, at least to some extent, a reflection of personality. When one comes to consider the little extra flourishes and details which embellish the basic action, this is even more the case. Murderers choose to invent their infamies in ways that are determined by their temperament, to offer some justification for the violence and profanity of their behaviour and to give some symbolic value to their actions. It is indeed a creative act. A nasty creative act, but nevertheless both expressive and aesthetic in its design in a way that is essentially no different from the painting of a canvas or the writing of a book. Some murderers have even consciously aspired to the status of an artist, with a control of their craft, a panache and sense of style that can readily be appreciated.

I suspect that Brian would have found this argument a little pretentious and embarrassing. He might even have dismissed it with wit and scorn, but I also suspect that a little part of him would have been amused and heartened by the idea.

A BIBLIOGRAPHY OF BOOKS AND PRINTED WORKS AUTHORED EDITED OR PRODUCED BY BRIAN LANE

EPHEMERA FROM FLUXUS AND EXPERIMENTAL MUSIC EVENTS 1968–1970

'Rainbow Day, Brian Lane and The First Dream Machine'

BL himself has put into writing how the 'away-day' events organized by Gallery Number Ten—the name used on the early printed notepaper was 'Live Events' next to a large square—from end-1968 onwards came to be performed under that new collective name (Ref.10.). When Aberystwyth planned a three-day mini-festival of experimental arts they invited BL—some time during 1968—for an initial discussion of his proposals. "BL hastily wrote a synopsis of the three days on a train from London to Aberystwyth. When it was shown to Steve Mills of the Festival Committee he noticed that the title for day three's events read not 'The Rainbow Day, Brian Lane and The First Dream Machine' but 'Rainbow Day, Brian Lane and The First Dream Machine'. Who is Rainbow Day? he asked. And so a new name was adopted by the group and Rainbow Day had to be found. During the whole of the activity under this name the identity of Rainbow Day was known only to BL though she became a constant working companion."

001 'Live Events' / (untitled synopsis of early Fluxus performance) (c.1968) **Single sheet of Gallery Number Ten notepaper headed 'Live Events' with synopsis of a Fluxus happening; typed in red a listing of 19 leaflets by their title/event, 254x204.** *All of the leaflets listed were to become later part of the 'Fluxus Leaflet Concert' below.*

002 Business Card, 'Rainbow Day, Brian Lane and The First Dream Machine' (1968) **Card, printed in yellow (the group's name) and black (Gallery's name and address), 63x115.** *The card locates the group at Gallery Number Ten, Blackheath Village and also names at the bottom in smaller print Rainbow Day, Brian Lane and Michael Lumb. Michael Lumb dropped out a little later because of personal difficulties and never did perform with the group.*

003 Notepaper, 'Rainbow Day, Brian Lane and The First Dream Machine' (1968) **Single sheet of paper, 353x203, details as above.**

004 'Pavilions in the Parks Pilot Scheme', London SW3, Sept./Oct.1968 **Small announcement card for Sue Braden's Pavilion 'Under Zoning', with blue tissue paper folded over and printed in black 'With A Wave'; 57x101.**

Queen Elizabeth Hall Concert, October 1968

On October 8 1968, RD BL + FDM staged an important concert at the Q.E.H., London; the programme of which was in three parts
1. Programmed Electronic and Computer Music (Studio S2FM)
2. 'The Italian Rainbow' (RD BL + FDM)
3. 'A Journey in Accordance' (Gentlemen of The Quiet Pavement)

005 White announcement leaflet/flyer printed black and green, 251x200. RAINBOW DAY / BRIAN LANE / AND THE FIRST

DREAM MACHINE / PRESENT / A CONCERT OF / EXPERIMENTAL MUSIC / QUEEN ELIZABETH HALL / TUESDAY OCTOBER 8 1968 7.45 PM

006 Smaller white announcement leaflet/flyer printed black and grey, 210x113; for same event and similar to leaflet above, but with additional lines describing programme: Featuring new works by / S 2F M / Rainbow Day, Brian Lane and the First Dream Machine / Gentlemen of the Quiet Pavement

007 Programme for event as above, eight stapled sheets of various sizes up to foolscap; plus signed photograph of RD and BL, title page as first item above for this event. *For the special edition of this programme several sheets were signed by the performers / artists and other participants in the event.*

008 Three posters for QEH Concert 1968 Screenprinted posters based on photographs of BL and Rainbow Day also adapted for other events.

Studio Theatre, Oval House Concert, November 1968
"During 1968 RD BL + FDM used the auditorium at Oval House for experiment / rehearsal. In gratitude the group presented a series of events between November 13–17 1968".

009 Programme for event, six stapled sheets of various sizes, white title page, 230x203. RAINBOW DAY / BRIAN LANE / AND THE FIRST DREAM MACHINE / Present an Afternoon of / MUSIC / Saturday November 16 2–4 pm / STUDIO THEATRE / Oval House Kennington Oval SE11

010 Double-gatefolded announcement card for a performance, 50x100, with b&w images. A performance of the / TRILOGY / of Maurene Sandoe / Nutcracker / Forest / Boxes / Oval House Kennington Oval SE11 / Sunday November 17 8.00 pm. *This announcement*

card was adapted for a repeat performance at Aberystwyth (061).

011 Small white announcement leaflet, printed orange and black, 126x50. Text below two circles printed in orange. JACOBS LADDER / Oval House will be turned into a Circle of Light by Jacob's sonic alchemy and magical movements placed in dramatic conjunction with the planet 'circularity'. The stars are right.

Aberystwyth Arts Festival, November 1968
'Rainbow and The Fluxus Leaflet Concert' (1968, 1970)
First performed by 'Rainbow Day Brian Lane and the First Dream Machine' at the Aberystwyth Arts Festival in November 1968 'The Fluxus Leaflet Concert' was recreated by BL and Maurene Sandoe / Probable Latitude (sans 'Rainbow Day' !) for the Great Georges Project Liverpool in May 1970 possibly in a somewhat revised and enlarged form. "Dedicated to 'Fluxus in general and to Ken Friedman and Ben Vautier in particular". "Printed leaflets are showered onto the the audience instructing them to take various actions to realise a series of visual and phonetic poems. Special effects made use of tape / slide / film sequences and the ... light show provided the effects for the 'Party' and 'War' sections."
BL's notes speak of 44 leaflets having been used at the (later) event, plus a poster. This tallies with the surviving set as described below. The line breaks of the texts are as shown here, and so is the use of upper and lower cases, but the list does not attempt to replicate the distinctive layout or typography of the material.

012 White announcement leaflet / flyer, printed in black and red, 202x165. RAINBOW DAY / BRIAN LANE / AND THE FIRST DREAM MACHINE / Present the / FLUX-

CONCERT / THE PARISH HALL / November 28 8pm / Aberystwyth Arts Festival 1968

013 Pink leaflet fragile / thin paper, printed in black, 178x127. THIS IS A FLUXUS CONCERT. / All information will be conveyed by Leaflet. / Obey all instructions immediately. / During the course of the concert you will be / privileged to be able to create FLUXoriginals— / works of art of unrivalled beauty. These are / FLUXapproved masterpieces and should be / kept and framed. / OBEY ALL INSTRUCTIONS. / OBEY THEM IMMEDIATELY.

014 White leaflet, printed in black, 204x128. You will find placed around the walls a / number of waste paper bins. / Place this leaflet in any one of them but / do so without damaging it in any way. / The leaflets will then be collected and / used at the next concert where they will / be collected and used at the next concert.

015 Small white leaflet, printed in red and black, 101x166. FREE !! C.I. DANCE TICKET / Please put on your hats throw your / streamers and dance / FLUXUS hopes you will enjoy yourselves!

016 Buff envelope, printed in red, 90x152, still sealed possibly containing (from holding against light !) streamer and paper hat (?). FREE !! C.I. DANCE TICKET

017 White leaflet, printed in black, 130x204. FIRST RAINBOW EVENT / Tear this page into small pieces and scatter / into the central fan.

018 Buff envelope, printed in black, empty, 89x162. SECOND RAINBOW EVENT

019 White leaflet, printed in black, 203x127. SECOND RAINBOW EVENT / Hold the contents of the envelope lightly / while listening to the music.

020 White leaflet, printed in red and black, 204x166. CAUTION / ART / CORRUPTS

021 Pink leaflet, rubberstamped in blue/black, 190x127. URGENT

022 White leaflet, printed in black and red, 204x130. FIRST FLUXmasterpiece / To make this authorized FLUXmasterpice / stick the coloured paper in appropriate / squares. / This work has already been signed and / authenticated and only needs framing / RED YELLOW BLUE / Fluxus Approved

023 Tiny buff envelope, printed black, 58x58, containing three gummed squares of coloured paper: red, yellow and blue. FIRST FLUXmasterpeice (sic)

024 White leaflet, printed in black and red, 204x121, with stylized face of Brian Lane. This is your second FLUXmasterpiece. / It needs only your signature. This work is / authentic only if you sign NOW! / Fluxus Approved

025 White leaflet, printed in black, 102x165. THIRD FLUXmasterpiece / Stick the labels onto any object you choose / and it will become a fully authorized / FLUXmasterpiece

026 Tiny buff envelope, printed black, 58x58, containing two gummed labels. THIRD FLUXmasterpiece / FLUXUS APPROVED MASTERPIECE

027 White leaflet printed in black 204x135 with stylized portrait of Brian Lane. FLUXpin-up Number One

028 White leaflet, printed in black, 204x120, with images of Brian Lane. FLUXpin-up Number Two

029 White leaflet, printed in black, 132x204, with image of rotting corpse. FLUXpin-up Number Three

030 White leaflet, printed in black, 204x114, drawing of elaborate personal scales. TRY YOUR WEIGHT

031 White leaflet, printed in black, 216x102. Only one person knows at first

032 White leaflet, printed in red, 83x216. BUILD SOMETHING / BIG

033 White leaflet, blank, small hole punched in top right hand corner, 203x166.

034 White leaflet, blank, small red dot in top right hand corner, 204x165.

035 White leaflet, printed in brown/russet, 203x129. PURPLE SMOKE COMES AT

036 White leaflet, printed in blue, 204x165. The sky is at least as blue as it is sky

037 White leaflet, printed in black on green field, 253x102. 'such flowers allover the place'

038 White leaflet, printed in green, 191x126. Ben Vautier hopes you are enjoying the play

039 White leaflet, printed in black, 216x141. PLAY BEETHOVEN ON / PIANO / (IT'S HIS YEAR!)

040 White leaflet, printed in black, 216x145. NOW PLAY SOME DRUMS

041 White leaflet, printed in black and red, 103x165. FIRST PHONIC POEM FOR RAIN-BOW / your letter is / R / speak this letter aloud and repeat at / 7 second intervals

042 White leaflet, printed in black and blue, 103x166. FIRST PHONIC POEM FOR RAIN-BOW / your letter is / B / speak this letter aloud and repeat at / 7 second intervals

043 White leaflet, printed in black and green, 102x166. FIRST PHONIC POEM FOR RAINBOW / your letter is / G / speak this letter aloud and repeat at / 7 second intervals

044 White leaflet, printed in black and green, 102x166. FIRST PHONIC POEM FOR RAINBOW / your letter is / O / speak this letter aloud and repeat at / 7 second intervals

045 White leaflet, printed in mauve and green, 216x101. DESTROY / TREES

046 White leaflet, printed in mauve and red, 216x101. DESTROY / HOUSES

047 White leaflet, printed in mauve and green, 216x101. DESTROY / GRASS

048 White leaflet, printed in mauve and red, 216x101. DESTROY / RED

049 White leaflet, printed in mauve and black, 216x101. DESTROY / DEATH

050 White leaflet, printed in mauve and black, 216x101. DESTROY / ART

051 White leaflet, printed in black, 211x129. WAR GAME / The pictures you are about to see are / silent. You have been provided with the / materials to make a sound track. / FLUXUS bids you fight well. / God is on your side.

052 Buff envelope, printed in black, 101x230, still sealed, (contents three long thin pieces of board ?). WAR GAME 3

053 Beige leaflet, printed in black, 190x126. BURN THIS PIECE OF PAPER NOW ! / Set fire to point X and allow flame to / spread to this line

054 White leaflet, printed in black and red, 203x166. YOUR / COLOUR / IS / PLEASE MOVE INTO THE AREA / MARKED / RED

055 White leaflet, printed in black and blue, 203x166. YOUR / COLOUR / IS / PLEASE MOVE INTO THE AREA / MARKED / BLUE

056 White leaflet, printed in black, 120x113. THIS FLUXUS LEAFLET CONCERT IS NOW / ENDED. / PLEASE LEAVE QUIETLY AND / RESPECTFULLY. / Please do not hesitate to write for details / of our home masterpiece kits. / Gallery Number Ten / 10 Royal Parade Blackheath Village London SE3 England

057 Poster, printed in red and black, texts in two squares, 510x190. A / LEAFLET / CONCERT / FLUXUS AT / GREATGEORGESPROJECT / Friday May 8 at 8.00 / Tickets 5s 0d from ROY 5109

Poetry Events at Aberystwyth Arts Festival, November 1968

058 White catalogue, printed in black and red, 202x165; title page, followed by two sheets of foolscap, listing by country, artists and works included. RAINBOW DAY / BRIAN LANE / AND THE FIRST DREAM MACHINE / Present an exhibition of / INTERNATIONAL / GRAPHIC / POETRY / THE PARISH HALL / November 27–29 / Aberystwyth Arts Festival 1968

059 Stapled to above, a smaller leaflet, printed in black, 127x101, with concrete poem. your / alphabets / are / WORDS

060 White announcement leaflet / flyer, printed in black and red, 202x165. RAINBOW DAY / BRIAN LANE / AND THE FIRST DREAM MACHINE / Present an exhibition of / POEM EVENTS / THE PARISH HALL / November 29 8pm / Aberystwyth Arts Festival 1968

061 Double-gatefolded announcement card, for a performance, 50x100, with b&w images. A performance of the / TRILOGY / of Maurene Sandoe / Nutcracker / Forest / Boxes / Aberystwyth Arts Festival 1968 / Friday November 29

062 Programme notes/handout, for performance of Maurene Sandoe's 'Trilogy', three stapled sheets, 110x203, with b&w drawings/graphics. nutcracker maurene sandoe / forest maurene sandoe / boxes maurene sandoe

063 Small leaflet, printed green and black, 112x88. FIN / by JOCHEN GERZ / D'une lecture / Du monde / A une autre lecture / D'un monde / De la lecture / A un autre monde

064 Small booklet, 72x128, printed front and rear covers with seven, intensely coloured, but blank leaves, stapled. THE BOOK OF THE / SILENT RAINBOW / Aberystwyth Arts Festival 1968

065 Small white envelope, 59x98, containing card, printed red flower (no text).

066 Small white envelope, 59x98, containing white card, blind embossed text. DARKNESS

067 Catalogue of blank pages, in printed envelope, 90x150, produced to coincide with the exhibition of herman de vries's white poems at the Festival.
Illustrations of de vries's white poems.

Hebden Bridge Festival, Yorkshire, April 1970
"A visual poem in red and yellow through the medium of a large number of small spheres of each colour floated on two sources of moving water. The location was ideal for running almost in parallel is the Calder a fast moving rocky river and a slow moving long-boat canal. The yellow spheres were floated on the canal and the red spheres on the Calder. The activity was preceded by the distribution without explanation of the two leaflets (separately) red and yellow."

068 Red leaflet, 75x260. Red with menace

069 Yellow leaflet, 125x160. There were quiet yellow voices on the water

070 Poster, 320x410. n.s. (10.) announcing: Parade leading to Calder Homes for 'Flags Bells Wind and Some Quiet Sounds' by Brian Lane

London New Arts Laboratory, April 1970

071 Programme/Listing of Events at London New Arts Laboratory, 14–25 April, 1970 Duplicated sheet, 203x253, mauve ink, with drawing of masked and costumed performer.

072 Invitation card, printed in black, 88x114. You are invited to the / BLACK AND WHITE / TEA PARTY / For Herman de Vries the memory of Ad Reinhardt / and Mary whose birthday it is. / 20.00h. Tuesday April 21 1970

073 The Seven Seals, Brian Lane (1970) Booklet made of seven sealed printed envelopes, 102x235, with printed short texts enclosed, single metal fastener, ed.100. (?). *Booklet produced for event/performance at above venue to be handed out to audience who would be instructed by presenter to open envelopes one by one to last.*

Great Georges Project, Liverpool
May 1970

'Red Roses for Lorca', 1970
Devised as a poem event for Great Georges Project Liverpool by BL and Maurene Sandoe. Realized at Great Georges Project on May 1 1970. "A quiet sort of street event." The event included the distribution of leaflets to the audience : BL's notes speak of 15 leaflets though 18 leaflets have been identified as belonging to this event. However two of the leaflets appear in two colour variants—both listed here—of which presumably only one of each was used. (MS confirms that 16 leaflets were used for 'Lorca'). There are also two posters.

Prototype Folio
There was discussion of producing a de-luxe folio containing the leaflets posters and photographs and supplementary texts to be published by Probable Latitude. Designed by Maurene Sandoe three final mock-ups were produced—one for the organizer Bill Harpe the other two were retained by BL and MS. **Printed card, cover with double gate-fold, opening to 240x1200; printed inscription in the form of a memorial card to Lorca "This book is to be for his memory". Pockets contain the full set of leaflets, both the 'Rose' and 'Oh Lorca' posters and two photographs.** The folio was never realized beyond these (three) dummies.

074 White slim leaflet folded along top edge, printed in black, 64x204. *Q. What does your divine rejoicing heart hold? A. A ringing of bells lost in the mist.*

075 Red slim leaflet folded along top edge, printed in red and white, 64x204. *Q. What*

do you feel in your mouth scarlet and thirsting? A. The taste of the bones of my big skull.

076 White slim leaflet folded along top edge, printed in black, 64x204. *Q. Who showed you the path of the poets? A. The fountain and the stream of the antique song.*

077 White leaflet, printed in red, 126x203. *Ah Harlem ! Ah Harlem ! Ah Harlem ! / There is no anguish to compare with / your oppressed reds or with the shud- / der of your blood within the dark eclipse / or with your garnet-coloured violence / deaf and dumb in the half-light or with / your great imprisoned king in a com- / missaire's uniform.*

078 Dark mauve leaflet, printed in red text outlined by triple-line borders, 126x203. *Variant of leaflet above with identical (but somewhat less readable) text. "This was the original design but paper was too expensive for bulk production." (MT)*

079 White leaflet, printed in black and red, 203x127; printed with a scattering of fleuron's in red to simulate flowers. *THE WHITE FRONT OF YOUR SHIRT BEARS 300 ROSES*

080 Orange leaflet, thin white Indian paper inked orange and printed in white, 127x188. *I want the skull's teeth to shine and yellows to flood the silk*

081 Black leaflet, printed in white, 202x128. *I want to sleep for a while a minute a century but all must know that / I have not died that there is a stable of gold in my lips that I am the / little friend of the West wind that I am the immense shadow of my tears*

082 White leaflet, printed in black, ambiguous drawing of tree roots or branches, 199x123. *THE WATER WAS BLACK WITHIN THE BRANCHES*

083 White leaflet, printed in black, ambiguous drawing of a tree root or branch, 204x128. *THE BRANCHES DIE OF LOVE*
084 White blotting paper leaflet, black text

above grey/black painted background, 202x126. My flesh and clothes are turning black like jet

085 White leaflet, printed in black and grey, minimal drawing of mountain, 203x127. and / THE HORSE ON THE MOUNTAIN

086 White leaflet, printed in green, same text on both sides, 127x195.
green green I love you green green green I love you green green green I love you green

087 Grey leaflet, white text, small pink mountains printed along bottom edge, 125x203. A thousand glass tambourines wounded the daybreak

088 White leaflet, printed in red and white, 203x126; barely visible shower of tiny flowers/fleurons, printed white on white. WARN THE JASMINES WITH / THEIR SMALL

WHITENESS

089 Yellow leaflet, printed in green, 127x203. I RESIST A SUNSET / OF GREEN POISON

090 Folded white leaflet, (folds along top and bottom edges) printed in grey, 107x127. Ya no me encontraron / ? no me encontraron ? / No. No me encontraron

091 Folded grey leaflet, (folds along top and bottom edges) printed in grey and black, 109x127. *Colour variant of leaflet above, identical text here with additional white border lines. "This was the original design but proved too difficult to produce in bulk." (MS)*

092 White poster, printed in black, 508x190. OH / LORCA

093 White poster, printed in red, 508x190. ROSE

BOOKS AND PRINTED WORKS 1966–1971

**Gallery Number Ten
Blackheath Village, London SE3**

101 Concrete Poetry (1966) **Announcement card for opening exhibition of Gallery Number Ten; card with two folds for standing up, printed in orange and black, 131x200.** *With map of location of gallery in Blackheath Village.*

102 Concrete Poetry 1966 **Catalogue of group show, 28pp and covers, 210x255, lp, in colour.** *Includes T.A.Clark, J.Furnival, A.Riddell, Bob Cobbing, D.S.Houedard, E.Morgan, et al.*

103 Fantastic Art (1966) **Catalogue of group show, 42pp, in soft covers, 129x191, lp.** *Lists two paintings by BL*

104 Abstract in Relief by Jack Ray (c.1966) **Catalogue, 10pp, in soft covers, 127x192, lp, coloured backing papers.**

105 Maurene Sandoe: mountains and other paintings 1966 **Invitation card, fc, 87x183, lp, with illustration.**

106 Maurene Sandoe: mountains and other paintings 1966 **Catalogue, 10pp, in soft covers, 180x128, lp, st, with illustrations.**

107 Brigid Marlin: Inscapes / The upside-down backwards and sideways art of Peter Holland (1967) **Catalogue of two-person show, 40pp, in soft covers, 128x192, lp, black ink on white paper, or white ink on grey paper.** *PH's section accessed by turning publication upside down.*

108 Robert Tiling: Paintings and Drawings (1967) **Catalogue, 16pp, soft covers, 128x193, lp, st, white paper, interleaved with grey sugar paper.**

109 Ex Tracts From The Compendium, Ian Breakwell (1967) **Two invitation cards: the larger one announcing the show, a piece of torn and printed grey card stuck-on,**

81x126; the smaller one inviting to the opening and a reading from his writings on opening day 43x81.

110 Music, Cavan McCarthy (1967) **20 printed cards, in wallet, 80x70, to be used in making a phonetic poem;** n.s. (10.18.)

111 one-word poems, Jiri Valoch (c.1967) **Prototype booklet, 15 leaves, in folder, typed and printed, 150x108, "design by Maurene Sandoe".** *Probably never realized as an edition.*

112 Eight Texts + One, Jean-Francois Bory; Editions Gallery Number Ten 1967. Co-publication with Contexte Paris. **Large paperback, 210 x189.** *Concrete texts/poems.*

113 Poeme Mathematique Baroque, Edgardo Antonio Vigo; Contexte, Paris, (c.1967). "Collection dirigee par J.F. Bory en conjonction avec Brian Lane Londres." **Folder, with three prints on coloured papers, with cutouts, 212x192.**

114 poemi concreti, Luigi Ferro (1970) **Announcement card, Ip, and blue square, 101x127.** *"The first of a new season of exhibitions of International Poetry. Opening Event: Maurizio Nannucci—Electronic Music"*

115 poemi concreti, Luigi Ferro (1970) **Folded catalogue of exhibition held at Gallery Number Ten; two folds, 102x132, Ip, with blue square and illustration of 'Iconogramma'.**

Project 67, Gallery Number Ten London SE3

Edited by Brian Lane and Trevor Wells

116 Plein Signe, Jean-Francois Bory (1967) "a semiotic story" **32pp, 210x130, Ip, inserted loose leaf into a stiff boxcover.** n.s. (1.10.)

117 Arithmetic Texts, Jean-Francois Bory (1967) **Collection of 18 visual texts, in envelope; printed litho and Ip, 150x230.** n.s. (1.10.) *reprinted 1980 as part of '69/70 for 79/80' in reduced format.*

118 Perpendicularly to the Plane of Letters: A Mirror, Julien Blaine (1967) **Silkscreen and Ip, in a folder, containing booklet of texts, working drawings, mirror illustrations and mirror 230x135.** n.s. (1.10.)

119 The Arrow Syndrome I, Trevor Wells (1967) Visual text originally published as an exhibition catalogue 'The Arrow Syndrome' at Gallery Number Ten April 1967. **7pp, silkscreen and Ip, 60x130.** n.s. (1.10.)

120 The Arrow Syndrome II, Trevor Wells and Brian Lane (1967) Printed in conjunction with 'The Arrow Syndrome' at Gallery Number Ten. **Tube containing five arrow prints in black, white, blue, red and yellow; silkscreen printed, 380x510; printed yellow 'luggage-label' with eyelet tied to tube.** n.s. (1.10.) *reprinted 1970 for Probable Latitude.*

121 Balcon Programme, Simon Cutts (1967) **Booklet, 12pp, 114x179, Ip.** Three poems: *'Lantern Couds' 'Sans mot'* and *'The Illustrated Garden'.*

122 A note on Lantern Clouds and Balcon Programme, Simon Cutts, 1967 **Explanatory notes to accompany the performance at the Institute of Contemporary Arts, London, October 1967; booklet, 6pp, duplicated, stapled into blue covers, 122x210, ed.50.**

123 Project 67 at ICA (1967) **Eight duplicated leaves, in printed envelope, 102x230.** *Introducing the performing artists/writers: J.-F. Bory, Julian Blaine, Ian Breakwell, Simon Cutts, Brian Lane, Adrian Nutbeem.*

124 Three untitled prints 1967 **Letterpress in two (one in three) colours, each 228x127.** *Illustrated on p.39 in catalogue "buchstaeblich woertlich" National Gallery, Berlin, 1987. The prints shown are similar in style to some of the Fluxus posters listed, e.g. 057.*

125 Flower, Brian Lane (1967) **Booklet, "a love story" red acetate cover, 48pp, 205x99, printed five colours Ip, on various types and colours of paper, papers stuck on.**

126 Summit, Ian Breakwell (1967) **Printed card cover containing text and holding the colour slide of his own painting from which text was written, 152x102.** n.s. (1.10.)

127 Newspoems, Edwin Morgan (1967) **A collection of 30 newspaper poems; lp and litho, inserted, with an introduction by the poet, into a card cover, with loose-leaf spine, 152x127.** n.s. (1.10.)

128 Four Portraits of a Poet, Kitasono Katue (1967) **Visual text; three-fold concertina, with images, lp, 113x91, on l.h.s. stuck into printed folded card, 118x94.** *Published in conjunction with J-F Bory Paris; reprinted 1980 as part of '69/70 for 79/80' in reduced format.*

129 Woodcuts on Paper, Arvind Krishna Mehrotra (1967) **A collection of short poems; 24pp, lp, card cover with loose-leaf spine.** n.s. (1.10.)

130 The Fly's Trip, George Dowden (1967) **A long poem in Japanese style; lp, with 5 litho illustrations from Japanese scrolls, bound as a pull-out scroll between stiff cover boards, 203x127.** n.s. (1.10.)

131 Twelve Hour Meditation Poem, Trevor Wells (1967) **Folded card, printed lp and relief.** n.s. (2.26.) *Reprinted 1980 as part of '69/70 for 79/80' in reduced format.*

132 Flower, Simon Cutts (1967) **Folded card, two-colour lp, 58x202.**

133 Apparatus for the Observation of Miracles, Brian Lane (1967) **Card, lp and acetate.** n.s. (2.26.). *Reprinted 1970 for Probable Latitude.*

134 Plucked, Thomas A. Clark (1967) **Printed lp, on coloured papers, 88x150.** n.s. (2.) *Published in conjunction with Bo Heem E Um Press, Greenock; reprinted 1980 as part of '69/70 for 79/80' in reduced format.*

135 Character, Yasuo Fujitomi (1967) **Silkscreen print, 320x250, black on white, or grey on grey.** n.s. (2.26.) *Reprinted 1970 in*

more colour combinations for Probable Latitude.

136 Pan, Yasuo Fujitomi (1967) **Postcard, lp, 139x81.**

137 Au Pied de la Lettre, Jean-Francois Bory (Franc) 1967 **Poster, silkscreen print, black on white, 510x380.** n.s. (2.26.)

138 1 Total, Julien Blaine (1967) **Poster, silkscreen print, black on white, with cut-out, 510x380.**

139 Poem, Ken Friedman (1967) **Narrow strip poem printed 4 colour lp, contained in circular tube cover.** n.s. (2.26.) *Reprinted 1970 for Probable Latitude.*

140 Bestarium, Cat Parczewska (1967) **Photoprint, 405x560.** n.s. (2.)

141 line sails, Simon Cutts (1967) **Eight printed cards, in folder, 126x1020, lp in blue, poems.** *Reprinted in reduced format 1980 as part of '69/70 for 79/80'.*

142 Pour remercier la pluie au matin, Simon Cutts (1967) **Folded card, 209x127, two colour lp, poem.** *In Winter 1967 catalogue (Winter 1967 catalogue n.s. but quoted in Ref.(4.)).*

143 Les Baigneurs Sont Tous Partis, James Mackenzie (1967) **Fold-out poem, seven folds, 51x114 (folded) lp, in printed cover, 55x118.** n.s. (4). *Reprinted 1970 for Probable Latitude.*

144 Invitation Card, Bristol Arts Centre Gallery (1968) **Designed for opening event to exhibition of Gallery Number Ten publications under Project 67 imprint; 102x137, lp, with orange blob.**

145 Programme, Bristol Arts Centre Gallery (1968) **Designed for opening live event to show as described above; printed envelope, in red and black, 90x152, enclosed seven printed pieces of paper.**

146 Poster for Bristol Arts Centre Events, 1968 **500x380.** *Published by Gallery Number Ten.* n.s. (10.)

147 Opera, Hugh Shrapnel (1970) **Box fold-er, 270x220x20, containing 32 scores pro-duced by various media, in various sizes, ed.21.** *On bottom of box: designed by Brian Lane (but not published or distributed by BL).*

Probable Latitude 76° 15'
Longitude 113° 10' E, London SE3

Edited by Brian Lane
"1970 brought a change in name (for no other reason that Rainbow Day had become disenchanted with the world of avant-garde and had left to lead a normal life). The new name derived from H.P.Lovecraft's 'At the Mountains of Madness'."

FIRST SERIES (February 1970)
"Proposal. ... the first of a monthly series of multiple literary objects."

148 Boxes, Maurene Sandoe (February 1970) **White card box, 214x144x120, opening out to form a miniature stage, and containing two mechanised black boxes for the per-formance in miniature of the event 'Boxes' by Maurene Sandoe; includes visual sound score and stage directions.**

149 Boxes (Do-it-yourself version), Maurene Sandoe (February 1970) **Pack containing 380x510 blueprint, for construction of stage and mechanized boxes for the above event; includes visual sound score and stage direc-tions.**

150 BIW 1 (BFN) 2 WIB, Maurene Sandoe (c.1970) **White card box, 215x270x50, con-taining instructions prints, cut-outs and objects, connected with the Black and White Events of Maurene Sandoe; mixed media.**

151 Poem for Ad Reinhardt, Jiri Valoch (1970) **Silkscreen print on perspex, 300x300; also printed silkscreen on card, 250x250.** *Reprinted 1980 as part of '69/70 for 79/80' in reduced format.*

152 The Lettrist Year, Vladimir Burda (1970)

Series of eight cards of the seasons, in wal-let, four colour lp; 140x95. n.s. (3.) *Reprinted 1978 for Editions Brian Lane as 4 double-sided cards in envelope.*

153 An Image Chart for The Pre-Raphaelite Brotherhood, Glyn Pursglove (1970) "A poem game". **Pack containing play pieces, three colour lp, 200x200.** n.s. (3.)

154 The Great Fire of London 2, Brian Lane "A poster event". **Two colour silkscreen on heavy white paper, 380x510.** *Never realized* (Ref.10.)

155 Gamme de Gamma, Peter Mayer (1970) **Sequence of eight cards, two colour lp, with author's notes, in wallet, 92x142.**

156 White Truth Black, Ladislav Nebesky (1970) **Four cards bearing binary texts, two colour lp, in printed envelope, 82x120.**

157 Corsage Kit, Ken Friedman (1970) **Printed box, 128x63x25, containing materi-als for do-it-yourself corsages, two colour lp.** n.s. (3.)

158 Seascape, Nicholas Zurbrugg (1970) Three interpretations by Maurene Sandoe. **Five colour lp, with paper cut-outs, 300x30, (folded).**

SECOND SERIES (March 1970)

159 2 ships qui passent, Victor Gudgin (1970) **Visual poem booklet, 12pp, lp, 70x104.**

160 On My Face, Gerry Gilbert (1970) **Envelope, 75x104, containing four juxtapos-able text pages, lp, 64x90.**

161 Epithalamium, Gerry Gibert (1970) **Envelope, 75x104, containing ten double-sided juxtaposable leaves of text, three colour lp, 64x90.**

162 The, Gerry Gilbert (1970) **Envelope, 75x104, containing eleven juxtaposable text page,s lp, 64x90.**

163 On My Face / Epithalamium / The, Gerry Gilbert (1970) **The above three envelopes**

issued as presentation sets, contained in a printed folder, 102x120.

164 Thoughts to Music, Simon Cutts (1970) **Booklet, with stiff cover, in printed sleeve, 12pp, 130x105, two colour lp texts.**

Nos.165–169: Reprints from Gallery Number Ten "... which we feel to be of sufficient interest and relevance to merit reprinting. The following titles have been reprinted from the Winter 1967 catalogue."

165 Apparatus for the Observation of Miracles, Brian Lane (1970) **Card, with cut-out rectangle and acetate, lp, 118x102.**

166 Poem, Ken Friedman (1970) **Narrow strip poem, printed 4 colour lp, contained in circular tube cover.** n.s. (4.)

167 Character, Yasuo Fujitomi (1970) **Silkscreen print, 320x250 printed in four colour combinations: Red on Red, Grey on Grey, Black on White, Blue on Blue.**

168 The Arrow Syndrome, Trevor Wells and Brian Lane (1970) Printed in conjunction with 'The Arrow Syndrome' at Gallery Number Ten. **Tube containing five arrow prints, in black, white, blue, red and yellow; silkscreen, 380x510; printed yellow 'luggage-label' with eyelet tied to tube.**

169 Les Baigneurs Sont Tous Partis, James Mackenzie (1970) **Fold-out poem, seven folds, 51x114 (folded), lp, in printed cover, 55x118.**

170 First Colour Computer, Brian Lane (c.1970) **Single sheet, first printed as a contribution to the Italian magazine 'Geiger', lp, on card.** n.s. (10.)

171 'Colour Poem' for Denise, Glyn Pursglove (1970) **Two versions: 1. three-colour visual interpretation, 2. original text version; two printed cards, 216x94 and 203x94.** Published but never issued (Ref.10.)

172 Camouflages, Simon Cutts (1970) **Booklet, in printed sleeve, 14pp, lp,**

161x130 poems; on rear cover: "distributed by: Gemma Three" *"Published by Probable Latitude, distributed by Gemma Three" (Ref.10.): this was the first and only printing of this title (in contrast to No.183 below).*

Gemma Three, Welling, Kent

"Gemma Three is a continuation of the work of Probable Latitude."

"In late 1970 when Probable Latitude ceased publishing Maurene Sandoe took over the existing titles and added to them under the name of Gemma Three."

Only one list was issued 'First Series' (1971) which consisted of three new titles and seven former Probable Latitude titles. When stocks of a Probable Latitude title were exhausted—and presumably only then—MS would reprint the title adding "distributed by Gemma Three" to the name of the imprint Probable Latitude. To date the compiler has only ever seen 'reprints' of two of the seven titles, Nos. 176 & 181 and some or all of the other five titles may never have been reprinted.

173 A Minimal Monument, Jiri Valoch (1971) **Card construction in printed box, impression and two colour lp, 70x35x35.**

174 Balance Poem on the Centrifugal Land, Mieko Shiomi (1971) **A pack containing fac-simile script/designs for this theatre event; two colour litho and lp, 310x210.** *Reprinted 1980 as part of '69/70 for 79/80' in different format and size.*

175 Triangles, Ladislav Nebesky (1971) A play in three acts with prologue and epilogue. **Seven cards, in wallet, 110x70, two colour lp, in printed envelope.**

Reprints from Probable Latitude:

176 An Image Chart for The Pre-Raphaelite Brotherhood, Glyn Pursglove (1971) "A poem game." **Pack, containing play pieces, three colour lp, 200x200.**

177 Seascape, Nicholas Zurbrugg (1971)

Three interpretations by Maurene Sandoe. Five colour lp, with paper cut-outs, 300x30 (folded). n.s. (6.10.)

178 Boxes, Maurene Sandoe (1971) **White card box, 214x144x120, opening out to form a miniature stage and containing two mechanised black boxes for the performance in miniature of the event 'Boxes' by Maurene Sandoe; includes visual sound score and stage directions.** n.s. (6.)

179 Boxes (Do-it-yourself version), Maurene Sandoe (1971) **Pack, containing 380x510 blueprint for construction of stage and mechanized boxes for above event; includes visual sound score and stage directions.** n.s. (6.)

180 BIW 1 (BFN) 2 WIB, Maurene Sandoe (1971) **White card box, 215x270x50, containing instructions, prints, cut-outs and** objects, connected with the Black and White Events of Maurene Sandoe. Mixed media. n.s. (6.)

181 Corsage Kit, Ken Friedman (1971) **Printed box, 128x63x25, containing materials for do-it-yourself corsages, two colour lp.**

182 The Arrow Syndrome, Trevor Wells and Brian Lane (1971) Published to coincide with the exhibition 'The Arrow Syndrome' at Gallery Number Ten in April 1967. **A yellow tube containing five arrow prints, in black, white, blue, red and yellow; printed silkscreen, 380x510.** n.s. (6.)

183 Thoughts to Music, Simon Cutts (1971) **Booklet, with stiff cover, in printed sleeve, 12pp, 130x105, two colour lp texts; on rear cover: "distributed by: Gemma Three".** *Another reprint from Probable Latitude though not one of the seven listed by Gemma Three.*

BOOKS AND PRINTED WORKS 1976–1977

Small Editions Geneva, Geneva & London

"These small 'book' works were hand-produced in editions of 5 copies each, and each of the five were dedicated and given to friends; a manuscript record was kept by the artist of the locations of the editions, and each recipient had a photocopy of the document. Subsquent changes of owner/location were inserted onto the original document." *Photocopies listing the recipients for the first four titles have been placed in the Archive by Michael Lumb who was one of the recipients for each title.*

201 Ausweis, Brian Lane, March 29 1976 **Folded 'passport' in clear wallet, 80x110, ed.5 signed and numbered.** n.s. (10.)

202 Livre Jaune, Brian Lane, March 29 1976 **Transparent wallet, 140x97, containing a yellow tissue paper unbound book, 16pp,** 125x83, ed.5 signed & numbered. n.s. (10.)

203 Two Quartets, Brian Lane, April 9 1976 **8 colour cards, in folder, in clear wallet, 90x130, ed.5 signed and numbered.** n.s. (10.)

204 Red 6—for Wanda, Brian Lane, August 3 1976 **7 printed cards, in printed envelope, 65x110, ed.6 signed and numbered.** n.s. (10.)

205 Blue Yellow, Brian Lane, August 10 1976 **Colour poem in folder, in clear walle,t 90x130, ed.6 signed and numbered.** n.s. (10.)

Wyndham Rd, London SE5

206 Gary Gilmore Fan Club, Bumper Pack, Brian Lane (c.1977) **Astralux wallet, with printed text, 270x170; in wallet: member's file/index card; membership card, with printed plastic sleeve; T-shirt transfer for hot iron; button badge with photographic image 63 mm; red lead pencil gold-stamped 'Gary Gilmore Fan Club'.**

Editions Brian Lane
162 Wyndham Road, London SE5

INFORMATION SERIES ONE

"A continuing series of folded cards and wallets of cards issued irregularly ten per year." Numbered editions of 50 except for No.3: umbered edition of 20 only; "Cards are printed generally by letterpress on Astralux. Size 105x155." All issues are by/edited by Brian Lane.

301 Number One, Pour que la soupe arrive chaude a la tranchee (1978) **Four index cards, in Astralux wallet, three with pre-printed images stuck on.**

302 Number Two, Mr.Love's Hops (1978) **Folded card, printed text label stuck on.**

303 Number Three, Granatelli in Town (1978) **Ten index cards, in Astralux wallet, two with text, eight with pre-printed images stuck on.** *See also 'Information Series Four' in 'Works titled Information Series', and 'The Mystery of Issue No.3' in 'Further Notes on Information Series One'*

304 Number Four, Unidentified passengers on Board the 'Lady Moira' (1978) **Folded card, printed text and thermographed image.**

305 Number Five, The Asparagus Patch (1978) **Folded card, printed text and images.**

306 Number Six, How to dig (1978) **Folded card, printed title and image.** *According to Michael Lumb the illustrations for the two titles above are taken from 'The Vegetable Garden Displayed' The Royal Horticultural Society.*

307 Number Seven, It was useful to have her pencils sharpened (1978) **Folded card, printed image with caption.**

308 Number Eight, The Sigs Concert Party (1978) **Folded card, pre-printed card stuck in.**

309 Number Nine, Airships (Shadows) (1978) **Nine index cards, in Astralux wallet, one** with title, eight with pre-printed images stuck on.

310 Number Ten, The Land Tents (1978) **Folded card, pre-printed images stuck on.** *Clearly based on the earlier A4 sheet 'Against the Landscape', 1976, Ref.30.*

311 Number Eleven, War Calls (1979) **Folded card, printed text and musical score.**

312 Number Twelve, Beano (1979) **Folded card, printed text and pre-printed image stuck in.**

313 A Selection of five postcards from Information Series One (1978) **Five cards, in grey Astralux folder, printed title on cover, 110x150, ed.300.** *(images taken from Nos.2, 4, 6, 7 and 8); also alternative version of same cards in printed white envelope.*

314 War Calls 1978 **Postcard.** Version of 'Information Series One' Number 11, also used in some envelopes as part of 'A selection of five postcards'.

INFORMATION SERIES ONE—SUPPLEMENTS

315 Supplement One, The Pocket Gourmet Guide to Natural History, Brian Lane 1978 **28pp, 115x105, lp, 11 tipped-in illustrations, numbered ed.125, first 25 hand-tinted by Debbie Squires and signed by the author.**

316 Supplement Two, I—An Afternoon Tea Game, Brian Lane 1978 **16pp, 100x75, lp, ed.150.**

317 Supplement Three, Notes on Umpiring and Exercises (Extracts 1), Brian Lane (1978) **10 leaves, string fastener, 205x145, offset, all illustrations hand-printed with single rubber stamp, inked in different colours, ed.75 signed & numbered.**

318 Supplement Three, *(should be Four)* A Chat About Water Pipes and Reservoirs, Brian Lane (1979) **Folded sheet of paper, 170x123, xerox, illustrated, ed.150.**

THE FOG LOG COLLECTION

An occasional series of small collections of thoughts on fog.

319 Number One, Roald Amundsen's Fog Log (July–September 1903), Brian Lane 1978 **12pp, 105x110, lp & offset, ed.150.**

320 Number Two, Fridtjof Nansen's Fog Log (July–September 1893), Brian Lane 1978 **12pp, 105x110, lp & offset, ed.150.**

321 Number Three, Robert Scott's Fog Log, Brian Lane ("In Preparation" 1979) *Not realized.*

322 Number Four, A.E. Nordenskiold's Fog Log, Brian Lane ("In Preparation" 1979) *Not realized.*

323 The Spread of Christianity in Europe, Brian Lane Dec.1978 **Folded card, 150x105, lp, with colour photograph by Mick Williamson, ed.100.**

324 Conventional Methods of Shewing Objects In Nature, Brian Lane (1978) **Folded card, 140x100, with tipped-in chart, 130 x205, lp and offset, ed.150.**

GENERAL SERIES

325 Circular Displacement, Brian Lane, August 1978 "These drawings of 1975 suggest a sequential method of imposing a crop-mark onto grassland over a period of eight years." **12 leaves, 75x10,5 offset litho, ed.150.**

326 Linear Displacement, Brian Lane, August 1978 **12 leaves, 75x105, offset litho, ed.150.**

327 Bonnie and Clyde Stuff, Brian Lane, 1978 "Robbing from banks is Bonnie and Clyde Stuff ... but stealing from a blind person ... !" **Printed card and text, in wallet, 90x105, lp and thermography, ed.200.**

328 Quiet Yellow Sounds on the River / Red with Menace, Brian Lane (1978) **"A box containing one each of the red and yellow spheres used in the event of this title (realized at Great Blakenham, Suffolk, May 3**

1975) as it was taken from the river. The edition was dictated by the number of relics recovered from the river, approx.150." With printed text, 43x80x40; in addition an ed.10 in a specially bound box.** *See also Nos.068 & 069 from the earlier staging of the event at Hebden Bridge 1970.*

329 Some Improbable Openings, Brian Lane (1978) **24pp, 145x100, lp, eight illustrations of unlikely chess openings, numbered ed.150.**

330 Six Portraits of The Artist **"Six cards, 105x145, in a wallet, of the superimposition photographs by Debbie Squires of Brian Lane as J-R Soto, Rebecca Horn, Joseph Beuys, Remo Salvadori, Katharina Sieverding and Richard Serra." Offset and lp, numbered ed.200.** ("In Preparation" 1979) *Not published.* (Ref.12.)

331 Four Portraits of a Poet, Kitasono Katue 1978 "Originally published in 1967 by Gallery Number Ten London." **Three-fold concertina with images, 106x88, on l.h.s. stuck into folded card, 110x95.** *Not listed elsewhere.*

332 The Lettrist Year, Vladimir Burda, 1978 "Originally published in 1968 by Gallery Number Ten, London." **Four cards, in printed envelope, 115x162, lp, in four colours.** *Not listed elsewhere.*

333 Brian Lane Printed Works 1978, January 1979 **Catalogue, 16pp 146x105, grey paper covers with cut-out window.**

INFORMATION SERIES TWO, NUMBER ONE

334 Manifesto 1, Brian Lane (1979) **Photo album, six leaves, 180x160, lp and bromides stuck in, ed.25 numbered & signed.**

335 A Residual Mouse, Brian Lane (1979) **Folded card, lp and torn bromide print stuck in, 75x105, numbered ed.100.** 1978

336 First Post / Last Post, Brian Lane (1979) **Pair of artists stamps in folder, 155x90, lp, ed.150.**

337 69/70 for 79/80 (1979/80) "A New Year offering in the form of a reproduction of nine works published by BL during 1969/70. Works preserve their original formats (though some have been scaled down in size) and are in a folio. Edition of 100 (of which the first 50 were distributed as personal gifts)."
a) First Colour Computer, Brian Lane **Folded card, 123x52, four-colour lp.**
b) Twenty Four Hour Meditation Poem, Trevor Wells **Folded card, 50x60, blind lp on coloured papers stuck in.**
c) line sails, Simon Cutts **Eight cards, in folder, poems, lp, 110x81.**
d) Plucked, Thomas A.Clark **Folded card, 68x98, single words printed on four coloured papers stuck in.**
e) Four Portraits of a Poet, Kitasone Katue **Three-fold concertina, with images stuck into folded card, 110x95.** *Different from No.331 only by not having printed reference to earlier publication in 1967.*
f) Image Chart for the Pre-Raphaelite Brotherhoood, Glyn Pursglove **Nine loose printed labels and card with grid, small piece of paper with 'Instructions,' all in stapled see-through flimsy bag, 120x176.**
g) Arithmetic Texts, Jean-Francois Bory **Ten leaves in printed envelope, 116x162, printed 'concrete' images, lp and offset (?).**
h) Poem for Ad Reinhardt, Jiri Valoch **Black card, 140x204, printed in black on recto and in white on verso.**
i) Balance Poem on the Centrifugal Land, Mieko Shiomi **Three leaves in printed folder, 205x144, text and drawings, litho (?).**

338 Ceremonies, Brian Lane, 1979 "Number One of an occasional series of documents." **Folded Astralux card, original wedding photo of BL & Debbie Squires stuck in. 145x104, ed.100 numbered.**

339 Nature is life—Save it !, Brian Lane, 1979 **Eight cards in printed envelope, rubber-stamped images in two colours, 88x125,** **ed.2, numbered and signed.** *Not listed elsewhere.*

340 Stamps of Many Lands, Steve Wheatley (1979) (Album version) **16 artists' stamps in album, 110x145, lp, ed.350, numbered & signed.**

341 Stamps of Many Lands, Steve Wheatley (1979) (Approvals wallet) **as above in wallet, ed.200 numbered.**

342 Stamps of Many Lands, Steve Wheatley (1979) (1st Day Covers) **as above, ed.200 numbered.**

LITTLE XEROX BOOKS

343 Number One, Concrete, Ruth Wolf-Rehfeldt (1979) **12pp, 105x148, lp and xerox, ed.300 numbered.**

344 Number Two, Three Cheers, Steve Wheatley (1979) **12pp, 105x148, lp and offset, ed.300 numbered.**

345 Number Three, Eon Pulse, Karl Kempton (1981) **12pp, 105x148, lp and xerox, ed.300 numbered.**

346 Number Four, Hunting the Unicorn, Jesse Glass Jnr (1981) **12pp, 105x148, lp and offset, ed.300 numbered.**

347 Concrete Tree, Ruth Wolf-Rehfeldt, 1979 **Postcard, 148x105, lp.**

348 I am not responsible for art, Gabor Toth, 1979 **Postcard, 105x146, lp.**

349 A Christmas Colouring Book, Brian Lane (c.1979) **Folded card, 182x125, text and illustrations, in two colours.** *Not listed elsewhere.*

350 Kilroy Was Here, Peter Mayer, 1978/(1979) **16 playing cards and booklet, 8pp, in red covers, sewn, lp, in labelled box, 92x78, ed.50 numbered.** (?Ref. 11.)

351 Irrigation Ditch Women, Ken Saville (In Preparation 1980) **"lp and bromides, ed.50 of which 20 hand-tinted."** *Not published.* (Ref. 11. & 12.)

352 mobile / two structures / language piece III, Jiri Valoch (1981) Three booklets: 'hommage to sol le witt' 'mobile'and 'two structures' 16pp, 16pp, 12pp respectively, **142x106, lp, sewn, boxed ed.100 numbered.**

353 A Manual of Arms, Brian Lane (c.1981) **Eight cards, in printed envelope, 80x115, printed images on all cards.** *A pun on 'manual' and two different dictionary definitions of 'arm'.*

354 World Album of Artists Stamps, edited by Steve Wheatley and Brian Lane. **"Loose-leaf album of individually printed artist's postage stamps. 210x148, lp and offset, ed.1000 numbered."** ("In Preparation" 1981) *Not realized.* (Ref. 12.)

355 If You Go Down in the Woods 1981 **Silkscreen prints in folder.** n.s. (15.)

356 Requiem for The Dead of The Great Plague, Brian Lane (c.1981) **Set of six printed folders, 211x159, in black card box with titled spine; mixed media production: cutouts, acetates, various printing methods.** *"... arising from a poem written in 1970 and adopted for performance as a projected and phonetic poem." (Ref.(10.) p.55 c.1979). ... but clearly this publication did not yet exist in this resolved format then. Edition size unknown : are there copies other than the one in the Archive ? One of the titles typed out under "In Preparation" but then pasted over on the list prepared by BL in 1981 Ref.(12.). Image of 'The Danse Macabre / The Dance of Death' on cover of each folder also used in 'Dr.Death' catalogue 1981 (Ref.14) giving further corroboration of assumed date.*

357 The Poet's Friend, Brian Lane, n.d./c.1981 **Small notebook with leather support and strap with buckle, presented in box covered in marbled paper, 75x250; printed note with illustration stuck into inner lid:** "13,115. October 14, 1886. Note book to be attached to the sleeve or cuff. (From 'The Illustrated Journal of the Patent Office', 1886)" *There is a spare printed notebook laid in, and the whole production has the finished look of an 'edition' rather than the appearance of a prototype. Another title first "In Preparation" but then pasted over in Ref.(12.) and not seen again! Copy in Archive found with spare copies of 'Doctor Death' productions; however this item is not listed in 'Doctor Death' catalogue Ref.(14.).*

358 Tales from the Vienna Woods, Brian Lane, Vienna, August 1982. Edition of 35 numbered; bookwork in archive—described below—not part of edition but has the original rubbings (edition has photocopies of these instead). **Bookwork in hard-cover folio 186x255 with side-ties. Thirteen rubbings of tree barks on sheets of musical notepaper with six staves each sheet has stuck-on label 'Nature Study Notes' with handwritten name of tree. Sheets of newspapers guillotined to same size used as padding to fill folio.** *Not listed elsewhere.*

359 The Artist Publisher. A Survey by Coracle Press, Craft Council Gallery, London 1986. Catalogue, edited by Brian Lane & Simon Cutts. **264x220, 64pp, numerous illustrations.**

Doctor Death Ice White and the Black Circus, Windsor, Berks

BUTTON–BADGE WORKS, Brian Lane
"Boxed in sets with key illustration." The badge-works listed, except for No.366, are now in the Tate Gallery Archive.
Battle Dress: "... dozens of individual badges combining to reform into a classic page from the early American war comics. The whole set may be worn or sections of it—even single selected badges."

360 Old Soldiers Never Run (c.1981) From DC's 'Our Army At War'. **Full-colour 65-badge set, overall size 230x180.**

361 P.T. Boat Skipper Captain Storm (c.1981)

Full-colour 65-badge set, overall size 230x180. n.s. (14.). *The set in the Archive is a full-colour 90-badge set 300x210 loose in box.*

362 The Commies and Sgt. Sawyer (c.1981) **Black and white 71-badge set, overall size 260x180.**

363 Expendable Skipper (c.1980 ?) Full-colour **54-badge set, overall size 230x180, unboxed.** *Not listed elsewhere*

364 Captain Storm (c.1980 ?) **Full-colour 54-badge set, overall size 230x180, unboxed.**
This set has a different image from the other 'Captain Storm'. Not listed elsewhere.
The above two sets are in format of nine rows by six columns, whereas the first three sets above have alternating rows of even and odd number of badges, thus fitting together more closely—arguably a more resolved design: Were Nos.363

& 364 earlier prototypes and for this reason never boxed ? But why then do Nos.361 & 364 have different images ?

365 Space Suit (c.1981) 'Amazing Stories' (August 1928). **44-badge set in full colour to make up cover of space fiction comic.** *The set in the Archive is only a 14 badge fragment though the spaceman is complete. There is also another 10-badge fragment of an image from another—unidentified—space fiction comic.*

366 A Family Album (1981) **Boxed.** n.s. (15.)

CHRISTMAS CARDS
Brian Lane / Susan Dunkley

367 A Seasonal Tale, 1982 **A4 sheet folded twice to A6, cartoons with captions, 148x105.**

368 A cautionary tale, 1983 **Orange folder with folded sheet of cartoons, 105x212.**

DOCTOR DEATH ICE WHITE AND THE BLACK CIRCUS

This section is not meant to be a comprehensive bibliography of the productions and publications of BL's 'commercial' enterprise of the early 80s but mainly lists the sample of publications retained for the Archive. For the full range see Ref.(14.).
There is however also a boxed set of samples in the Archive with a checklist dated and signed "BL August 1981" addressed to the 'Galerie George De Ville', New Orleans, but for some unknown reason never despatched. BL's list itemizes 18 items included. This box of samples has been left as found.

Ice White Designs
162 Wyndham Road, London SE5

AUTOGRAPH COLLECTIONS
"These small thematic albums of facsimile signatures are an interesting complement to badge sets."

401 Number One, Kings and Queens of England (c.1980)

402 Number Two, Prime Ministers of Britain (c.1980)

403 Number Three, Presidents of America (c.1980)
Three booklets in uniform format, 69x150, handsewn, in pictorial coloured sleeves, 24pp, 36pp and 24pp, respectively; signatures, with names and dates in appendices.

404 Strange People (c.1980) A collection of 38 real photographs of celebrated FREAKS, culled from the famous 'Barnum & Bailey Museum' and the Ripley Bros. 'Believe It Or Not Show'. **Photographs are printed to size 150x90 and boxed in sets with biographical notes.** *The copy in the Archive is a boxed set mounted on cards 178x133, lacking No.34, 'Beano' which was used also as No.12 of Information Series One, Editions Brian Lane,*

1978; the biographical notes are also missing.

405 The Pentacles of the Planets (c.1980)
"A series of 8 cards each reproducing one of
the Pentacles of Power and Protection of the
Planets. The Pentacles are printed on the front
of the cards and embossed. ... Each card is
printed in the colour appropriate to the planet." **Eight folded cards, 210x99, in
envelopes.**

POSTCARD SETS

406 Diabolicards—A Demonology 1977. **10
cards, printed in grey (images) and black
(texts) as a set of illustrations from Colin de
Plancy's 'Demonologie' published in 1818.**

THE WITCH CARDS

A first series of 4 cards illustrated from early
manuscripts and books on the subject of
Witches and The Witch Trials.

407 Witch Feeding Her Familiars (c.1980) "A
woodcut from the 'Dialogue Concerning
Witches'." **Folded card, 108x152, in envelope.**

408 Mathew Hopkins—Witchfinder General
(c.1980) n.s. (14.)

409 The Chelmsford Witches (c.1980)
"Illustrated with the frontpage of a contempo-
rary (1589) pamphlet describing the trials of
Joan Cony Joan Upney and Joan Prentice."
Folded card, 209x101, in envelope.

410 Urbain Grandier's Pact with the Devils
(c.1980) n.s. (14.)

411 The Cemetary Dance (C.1980) "One of a
series of 63 panels designed by Caspard
Meglinger to decorate the Pont des Moulin in
Lucerne. The general theme of the design is
'the frailty of human life'." **Folded card,
108x152, in envelope, printed in mauve and
black.**

D.D., London

412 The Danse Macabre / The Dance of
Death (c.1980) "reproducing one of the illustrations from the 'Nuremberg Chronicle'

(1493)." **Folded sheet, 329x204 unfolded, in
envelope with black lines on outer edges,
101x228, flap sealed with black blob.**

413 Dance of Death Alphabet 1980
"Illuminated initials designed by Hans Holbein
the Younger and engraved by Hans
Lutzelburger Basle 1526." **Booklet in format
of titles 401 to 403, 24pp, 69x149, handsewn, in printed black sleeve.**

414 Infernal Punishment of The Seven Deadly
Sins 1980 "From 'Le grant kalendrier et com-
post de Bergiers' Troyes 1496"
a) **Booklet, 12pp, 131x106, handsewn, in
printed sleeve; reproductions of seven
woodcuts.**
b) **Folio of prints, loose in a printed card
folio, 180x153.**
c) **Hand-tinted set, "professionally hand-
tinted and mounted ready for framing",
251x191.**

415 Imagines Mortis 1980 "Cuts by the
design of Hans Holbein (the Younger)"
a) **Booklet, 12pp, 146x105, handsewn, in
printed sleeve; reproductions of eight
woodcuts.**
b) **Folio of prints, loose in a printed card
folio, 146x106.**
c) **Hand-tinted set mounted in pairs.**

416 The Papist Devil (c.1981) "Printed from a
Reformation handbill against Pope Alexander
VI; late 15th century". **Print, sheet size
280x196, printed "on artificially antiquated
paper".**

417 Death and the Lansquenets (c.1981)
"engraved in 1524 by Urs Graf." **Print, sheet
size 280x196, printed "on artificially antiquated paper"; Print, paper 280x196.**

418 The Annals of Newgate (c.1981) "The
first of a series of folios of extracts from this
celebrated document on the life crimes and
trials of the notorious criminals who passed
through Newgate." **Printed folder, 169x103,
enclosing various printed documents.**

419 Taoist Good-Luck Charm (c.1981) "Prepared by the Taoist priest as a charm claimed to cure all diseases the slip of yellow paper with its red script was to be burnt and the ashes drunk in liquid." **Printed folder, 210x111, enclosing printed Japanese handmade paper, 201x90.**

420 The Gettysburg Address (c.1981) "Facsimile of Abraham Lincoln's manuscript of his address at the dedication of the cemetery at Gettysburg November 19 1863." **Printed folder, 180x145, with two printed enclosures.**

421 Der Fuehrer. Eagle and Swastika motif designed for Adolf Hitler's personal correspondence. **296x209, printed in 'gold' relief.**

422 The 'Lusitania' Medal. The medal is mounted in box as two separate casts of obverse and reverse. **"Finely bound presentation case contains castings in metal-filled resin of the Lusitania medal with accompanying material ..."**

Doctor Death

423 Generals of the American Civil War 1981 **Booklet, 12pp, 123x103, handsewn.**

424 The Bullfighters 1981 **Booklet, 8pp, 135x122, handsewn.**

425 The Mobsters 1981 **Booklet, 12pp, 207x145, handsewn.**
Three examples of the booklets giving brief biographical notes on the people featured on the many different themed sets of button badges. Many such sets remain in the Archive.

Danse Macabre
Brian Lane, Belmont Hill, London SE13

427 Chorus from the Gallows, Brian Lane (c.1995) "An illustrated essay 'Some Notes on Street Literature' by Brian Lane. Including a set of 15 facsimile copies of Classic crime and Punishment Broadsheets." **Broadsheet, 16pp of A4.**

428 Frederick Baker and the Murder of Sweet Fanny Adams, Brian Lane, 1996 **Broadsheet, 12pp of A5, in handsewn printed paper covers, illustrations.**

429 'My Wife or My Life' the case of Robert Blakesley (c.1996) **Broadsheet, single sheet folded to A5, 4pp, contemporary woodcut illustration.**

The Murder Club

Christmas Cards / Booklets

430 Ordinances against a Set of Crack-brained Fellows, commonly called by the Name of Poets, 1986. **Four pages of text in brown covers, 178x125.**

431 Two Boxing Nights. A Seasonal Tale by Percy Mapleton, 1988. **Booklet, 12pp, 209x144, green paper covers, text with illustrations.**

WORKS TITLED 'INFORMATION SERIES'

During the mid and late seventies Brian Lane was thinking in series and often designated the results of his investigations—both in the form of unique works and of publications—as INFORMATION SERIES with a suitable system of notation. The long-term collaboration with Michael Lumb 'Lumb Lane' and its sudden dissolution late-1977 however made it impossible to maintain a strictly chronological or rational system of numbering.

All works listed are by Brian Lane and the unique works are now in the Tate Gallery Archive.

INFORMATION SERIES ONE
Nos.1–12, 1978–79, *published.*

INFORMATION SERIES ONE—SUPPLEMENTS
Supplements One to Four, 1978–79, published.

INFORMATION SERIES TWO, NUMBER ONE
Manifesto 1, Brian Lane (1979), published.

INFORMATION SERIES THREE, NUMBER ONE
Not yet discovered: may not have been realized.

INFORMATION SERIES THREE, NUMBER TWO

501 Guide Camp (c.1974/75) **Fifty index cards, in Astralux wallet: Title card, Index card and 48 numbered cards with original photographs stuck-on, typed captions unique work.** Card No.30 'Joke' lacks photograph.

INFORMATION SERIES THREE, NUMBER THREE

502 Unidentified People (General) 1 (c.1974/75) **Twelve index cards, in Astralux wallet: Title card, Index card and 10 numbered cards with original photographs stuck-on; unique work.**

INFORMATION SERIES THREE, NUMBER FOUR
Granatelli in Town, Lumb Lane, London and Henley, nr. Ipswich, July 1975. Designated thus on two dummy booklets at early stages of evolution of this title but published in different format by BL as Information Series One, Number Three in 1978.

INFORMATION SERIES FOUR
"The first direct collaboration of Lumb Lane and a joint extension of Brian Lane's continuous sequence of 'Information Series'. One sheet will be issued each month serving partly as a vehicle of communication presenting aspects of work in progress and partly for the presentation of observations and independent 'information." (Ref.(28.) c.1974/75. Michael Lumb's annotations question parts of the statement). There is a set of draft sheets in the archive for the first nine numbers planned but none were realized under this imprint. In due course the BL-authored numbers were to be

used for Information Series One published under the imprint Editions Brian Lane. Thus the final numbering for all Information Series does not follow chronological order. No further works designated INFORMATION SERIES are known.

Other publications designated as series:

THE FOG LOG COLLECTION
Nos.1 & 2, 1978, published;
Nos.3 & 4: listed in 'Printed Works 1978' as "In Preparation" but never realized.

CEREMONIES "an occasional series of documents"
Number One, 1979, published; other issues, each time involving Debbie Squires, were planned but never realized.

LITTLE XEROX BOOKS
Nos.1–4, 1979–81, published; other titles reached dummy staged but were not realized, possibly after editorial disagreements with their authors.

Further Notes on 'Information Series One'

1. The Distribution of 'Information Series One'
The following statement appears in the catalogue 'Brian Lane Printed Works 1978':
'Information Series One'
"A continuing series of folded cards and wallets of cards, issued irregularly, ten per year. This series is limited to 50 sets and is available on subscription only—each subscriber receiving the same number of each issue.
Price of subscription £20.00 ($50, DM85, FF170) which includes 1978 issues 1–10 and 1979 issues 11–20. Fifteen subscriptions only are available."
Note the '15 subscriptions only' out of a total edition of 50 (the edition size of most titles in the same list is 150 in a range from 75 to 200). Why this small number of subsriptions only ? The answer is to be found in the handwritten distribution list found among BL's papers (see 'Sources and References' Ref.8.)

2. Recipients of Free Copies

Page 1 of the distribution list for Numbers 1–12, simplifying slightly and leaving the various crossings-out unresolved, may be transcribed as follows:

1. Coracle Press, Nos. 1–12.
2. Michael Lumb, Ipswich, Nos. 1–12.
3. R.& P. Middleton, London, Nos. 1–7 only.
4. Stephen Duncalf, London, Nos. 1–12.
5. Madelaine Westwood, Beds. Nos. 1–7 only.
6. Oswell Blakeston, London, Nos. 1–12.
7. Elena Middleton, London, Nos. 1–12.
8. Galerie Ecart, Geneva, Nos. 1–12, except No.9 (?).
9. Carl Freeman, Geneva, Nos. 1–12, except No.3.
10. Debbie Squires, London, Nos. 1–12.
11. Ian Breakwell, Nos. 1–7 only, except No.3.
12. Joseph Beuys, Dusseldorf, Nos. 1–7 only, except No.3.
13. Bob Cobbing, London, Nos. 1–12, except No.9 (?).
14. T.& L. Clark, Nailsworth, Nos. 1–12, except No.3.
15. Philip Corner, NYC, Nos. 1–12, except Nos.3 & 9.
16. John Furnival, Woodchester, Nos. 1–12, except No.3.
17. David Brown, Tate Gallery, Nos. 1–12.
18. Dr. Diane Cumming, NZ, Nos. 1–7 only, except No.3.
19. Jochen Gerz, Paris, Nos. 1–12, except No.3.
20. Bill Harpe, Liverpool, Nos. 1–12, except No.3.
21. Seth Siegelaub / Les Krims, Nos. 1–12.
22. Kunsthalle, Bern, Nos. 1–7 only, except No.3.
23. Fluxus / G.Macunias, USA, Nos. 1–7 only (?).
24. Wide White Space / Ben Vautier, Nos. 1–10, except No.3 (?).
25. Rene Block / Franklin Furnace, Nos. 1–12, except No.3.
26. Martin Shakerley-Bennett, Suffolk, Nos. 1–7 only, except No.3.
27. Martin Simms, London, Nos. 1–7 only, except No.3.
28. Gregory Batcock / Rod Summers, Nos. 1–12 (?).
29. Mick Williamson, Maidstone, Nos. 1–12.
30. New Church Road Gallery, London, Nos. 1–10, except No.3.
31. Stuart Mills, Belper, Nos. 1–12.
32. David Briers, Cardiff, Nos. 1–12, except No.3.
33. Janos Urban, Lausanne, Nos. 1–12, except No.3.
34. Ian Gardner, Bradford, Nos. 1–12.

Allowing for an archive set the list above accounts for 35 sets, leaving the balance of 15 sets for subscription, in agreement with the text from the 1978 catalogue. In other words, the above distribution list was in fact BL's mailing list for Free Copies. No further issues of this series were produced hereafter.

3. Subscribers

Page 2 of the distribution list now in Debbie Squires' handwriting continues with sets 35–50

but only two more names are written in:

36. Jean Brown, USA ...(blank) ...
39. Jonathan Williams, USA, Nos. 1–12, except No.3.

We do not know whether, and for how long, these records were kept up to date, and it is conceivable that there were a few later subscribers. (In a letter BL later wrote of having mailed out over time between 80 and 150 copies of his 'Printed Works 1978' catalogue). However at end–1999, eight sets still remained in stock (all complete and collated except for Issue No.3). Allowing for the set presented by BL to the compiler back in 1985/86 we arrive at the maximum possible number of subscribers as:

$$50 - 34 - 8 - 1 = 7$$

A more realistic estimate might be for just three or four subscribers, and Debbie Squires has recently suggested a smaller number yet ("if any at all"). In his correspondence BL later claimed that his practice of making editions providing for a mix of free copies and sales "had worked reasonably well for Information Series One", but in the light of the evidence above BL's statement may well have been a little misleading as to sales !

4. The Mystery of Issue No.3 'Granatelli in Town'

As can be seen from the distribution list, half of all sets mailed are missing Number Three: there are positive records for just 17 copies of Number Three having been mailed out. Was there a problem about Number Three ? And who was Andy Granatelli ?

The published issue provides no explanation beyond the title and the source of the eight photographic images tipped-on to index cards: "The photographs of Andy Granatelli were taken by Maurice Rowe for an article in 'Motor', July 29 1972."

Not a single editioned copy remained in BL's files, but two 1975 dummies of 'Granatelli' have survived. Originally the title was to be published as part of the Lumb Lane project, and in BL's letter to Michael Lumb of 6.7.1975 accompanying one of the dummies he explains: "To put you into the picture; Andy Granatelli is the 'inventor' and big boss of the STP oil-additive company, coming from a squalid, no-shoes background to be millionaire at 30. I think in the choice of these portraits it has gone beyond the personal selection of Granatelli, in movement and expression. ... I am not sure whether I like Granatelli or not, which is perhaps the reason that I can use the portraits. I find no morality or immorality in the face—it is an almost unquantifiable image." The earlier of the two dummies—then still in the format of eight page booklets—gives the planned edition size, in pencil, as 20—later overwritten 25, while the later, typed dummy speaks of "an edition of 25 numbered copies". In the same letter BL explains "As for the edi-

tion of 25—they are all hand-made and I neither have the time nor the inclination to do a bigger one. (I thought of an edition of 2—as most of the other Information Series are, but it could be a useful thing to send around, so 25)".

Three years later, in 1978, a first edition of 20 copies was produced of 'Granatelli', albeit now in a revised format—ten index cards in a wallet—but with the same eight images tipped-on. Of course, it was no longer a Lumb Lane title, but part of BL's 'Information Series One', all other issues of which were produced in editions of 50. Why didn't BL produce 50 of the 'Granatelli' issue too, given that his catalogue had announced '50 sets' of the whole Series ?

5. The Mystery Resolved

The explanation turned up in the form of a pencilled 'Note' found among BL's papers: "Information Series One, Number Three has been reconstructed from xerox copies to complete all sets from 37–50. The images used to create the initial edition resulted from a chance find of 36 sheets of the original printings to be bound into the magazine Autocar. The reconstruction is effectively dated April 1986. Brian Lane."

This confirms that in all 20 editioned copies the photos are the actual newsprint cuttings! On closer inspection it appears the figure '36' was added later—there was a mere "—" at first: but 36 sheets would have allowed an edition of 36 rather than 20. (It appears that by 1986 BL was no longer concerned that at most just 20 of the first 36 recipients of the series had received Issue No.3. Note also the discrepancy as to the title of the magazine.) Clearly the planned reconstruction of sets 37 to 50 did not materialize in the end. Why not? The clue lies in a bunch of 14 photocopies of a collaged set of Granatelli photos found in the files: ready for cutting-out, and exactly the number required to complete sets 37 to 50. Each photocopied sheet has ten photos, but one of the eight photos required for 'Granatelli'—the largest of the eight—is missing on the sheet. The same photograph is missing from the set of magazine cuttings kept in a small envelope in the files. Yet a cutting of the missing photo had been pasted into the early dummy and could have been re-used for the photocopies. A mere oversight ? Just one more small job ? BL never did complete the reconstructions.

Index Card Works

For many works in the late seventies BL employed the format of index cards—usually A6 but sometimes A5—for his long-term projects and investigations. BL housed these works either in handmade cardboard boxes, or in library-style, plastic filing boxes with a hinged lid. All works listed are unique—except for No.507, and are now held in the Tate Gallery Archive.

THE GENEVA PROJECTS

503 When We Heard The News, 1977. **c.100 index cards, with handwritten texts & photos stuck on in black cardboard box, unique.** *The project covers the period from 3 March 1977 to 15 April 1977, when BL was based in Geneva, where Debbie Squires visited him (February 25 to March 21 1977). Each card is dated and, at the top, copies out in, BL's handwriting a news item of the day; below is a set of four photobooth portraits of BL and DS posing together that same day. From 21 March 1977, after DS had returned to London, the project carried on in Geneva and London on separate cards. Because DS did not live close to a photobooth, there are only three more cards of her, whereas BL kept the scheme going for a little while longer. A second, related set of index cards in the box has cut-out newspaper photos covering the same news items, with the date and name of the paper. According to DS the poses they struck were not determined by the news items of the day, which were selected quite*

separately: any connection therefore is in the reader's mind! BL elsewhere once wrote that the project had been about their relationship during that period. The project tallies in its dates with the entries and descriptions in BL's Geneva 'Diary', written to keep DS informed of the progress of his work while they were apart.

504 Small Flags – Geneva, (1977) **Large number of index cards, in two grey plastic filing card boxes with hinged lid, unique.** *The cards carry the names of the streets of Geneva: streets A–L in one box, M–Z in the other. The project involved BL and Debbie Squires walking towards each other from opposite ends of each street, each picking up one item of debris found underfoot, the 'Small Flags' of the title, which have been filed on the cards in stamp collectors' gummed clearview pockets. (Information obtained from Debbie Squires who was BL's collaborator on this project.)*

505 Due North of Geneva, (1977) **Large number of index cards, in orange-coloured plastic filing card box with hinged lid.** *Each card with the name of a street in Geneva—in alphabetical order—and with a photograph. Another aspect of the project above: at the point where BL and DS met in the street a photo was taken pointing the camera 'Due North'.*

506 Rue Francois Ruchon, (c.1977) **Set of 22 A4 photocopies—the originals have still to be located—with texts, photographs, captions, maps and scale drawings.** *Not strictly an index card work, but related to above Geneva projects: "documenting the tangible features of a street and its accessibility to essential services and shops". "Rue Francois Ruchon was chosen as being the most accessible test street to the writer, whose 9th floor studio looked down onto the street from the left-hand side."*

507 In Good Company, 1977–1978. **c.40 pre-printed index cards, 212x146, with photos stuck on, no box.** *The photographs (by*

Debbie Squires) always show BL 'in good company' of another person. The information recorded is Name, Date, Location, Occasion, Description and Signature. There would be two cards with identical photographs, recording separately the personal details of BL and his collaborators, who—in theory at least—would be given BL's card. Some cards have photographs but lack all personal details. The great majority of the photographs were taken at Coracle Press Gallery openings. (A full set may never have been collated, but what was probably the most complete set went with the Coracle Press archives to the Getty Museum.)

508 In Good Company, 1977–1978.
Large number of source and duplicate photographs for cards, as above with names on separate index cards, between alphabetical divider cards, in hinged, black cardboard box, 124x168x110, includes some photographs of unidentified people. *Some photographs show BL 'in the good company' of some worthy statues!*

509 Nature (Mort) Trail, 1978.
Eight pre-printed index cards, 128x204, with photographs stuck on, grey card wallet, unique. *Photographs of 'dead' objects taken on trail from Appledore to Ivychurch on July 8 1978, with handwritten description of objects photographed and map reference.*

510 Nature (Mort) Trail, 1978.
13 pre-printed index cards, 128x204, with photographs stuck on, grey card wallet, unique. *Photographs of 'dead' objects taken on the Ridgeway from Kingston Lisle on July 16 1978 with handwritten description of objects photographed and map reference.*

511 London Photographs, n.d.
Undated photographs between alphabetical divider cards, in hinged plastic filing card box. *Location and subject identified on back of photographs; enclosed is a handwritten piece of paper detailing walks during which specific photographs were taken (red underlinings).*

512 Empire Defenders, n.d.
Undated index card project, white cardboard box, no label, no date, unique. *Nineteen index cards, nine of them (numbered) with original coloured bubble gum cards from a series published in 1941 titled 'Empire Defenders'. The other cards are in BL's neat handwriting copying out the text on the back of the cards.*

513 Empire Defenders n.d.
Undated index card project, black cardboard box, no label, unique. *c.73 index cards with esoteric details of military items in the format of photographic enlargements from war comic-style images stuck on, top left-hand corner with typed title. Cards sorted into alphabetical order from Accompaniment (musical), Arm and Badge to Wall, Weapon and Window.*

514 Trois Phases Successives De La Destruction, Par La Artillerie, De L'Aubarge De Dry Grachten, n.d.
Undated index card project, white cardboard box, no label, unique. *Four cards, three of which with pre-printed images of the building of the title in three stages of cumulative destruction by war action.*

515 Shaving, n.d.
Three index cards: title card and two cards, with postcards stuck on with photographs of WWI soldiers shaving, undated, unique.

516 (Untitled) Soldier with Field of WWI Shell Casings, n.d.
Four index cards without title, stuck on each card—flush with l.h.s. edges—is part of a photograph of a single soldier posing in front of a field of discarded shell casings, the four pictures together making up a panoramic shot of the scene; no captions, undated, unique.

517 A Manual of Arms (c.1980) **Eleven index cards of which nine have stuck on images of men holding up 'arms'.** *Prototype of the work that was to be published later, in 1981, with the* same title, *as eight printed, smaller cards in a printed envelope.*

Three other works employing index cards have been listed already under the heading of 'Works titled INFORMATION SERIES', including the published series, 'Series One'.

SOME WORKS IN HOMAGE TO BRUCE NAUMAN

Sorting the many boxes of BL's papers and files the compiler was surprised by the number of works coming to light relating to, or produced in homage to, Bruce Nauman's work. Though most of these works must have been produced for eventual publication—there are multiple copies of several works ready for distribution—none were ever listed by BL and few people will have been aware of these works. The unique works and copies of all 'editioned' works are now in the Tate Gallery Archive. Found among BL's books was an early catalogue of Bruce Nauman's work: 'Bruce Nauman', Leo Castelli Gallery, New York, 1968. Catalogue, 280x217, 12pp, grid lay-out of four works per page, all 44 works illustrated.

But probably the key source for BL's work was another catalogue found among his books: 'Bruce Nauman', Kunsthalle Bern, 1973, Catalogue, Los Angeles County Museum of Art, 1972/73, subsequently travelling to six other museums in the USA and Europe; 240x202 186pp, numerous illustrations; p.71: 'Untitled (Set of 11 color photographs)' 1966–67, four of the ten photos listed 'A' to 'J' are illustrated including: 'J: Self Portrait as a Fountain'. It seems likely that BL did see this show in Bern during his second extended stay in Geneva, as there is an envelope in the files marked "Bruce Nauman Kunsthalle Bern" with three photographs of abstract, floor-based sculptures.

601 'Self-Portrait as a Fountain Bruce Nauman' "Attach this plaque to an anthropomorphic fountain", Brian Lane (c.1976/77)

Printed single piece of card, 95x124, with Bruce Nauman's photo of his 'fountain' performance. *(i.e head tilted backwards spewing water in an arc from pursed lips) and the caption/ instruction of the title. The image seems copied 1:1 from the 1973 catalogue above. A bundle of 59 copies of this printed card—or 'plaque'—was found among BL's papers. There would almost certainly have been copyright problems, and caution may have prevailed.*

602 ditto: framed copy of same card. **88x97, image of Bruce Nauman and title of photo neatly cut-out from card above.** *BL's personal copy re-using old frame (88x97) and an earlier card within as a mount.*

603 'Bruce Nauman' Plaque, Brian Lane (1977) **Small brushed aluminium plaque engraved 'Bruce Nauman', the letters painted black, mounted on piece of light-brown wood, 42x94, in black card box, 152x102, unique.** *The design for this plaque is sketched, and the Nauman project described, in BL's Geneva 'Diary' (described more fully in 'Some Unique Objects and Bookworks').*

604 Photographs of Fountains with BL's 'Bruce Nauman Plaque' attached (1977). **Assorted photographs in 'Airmal' envelope with biro title 'Bruce Nauman'; also contact prints.** *Photographs taken (by Debbie Squires) when BL and DS visited a number of locations (Geneva and Chamonix are identified on back of photos) seeking out suitable fountains, to which they would temporarily attach the Bruce Nauman plaque. A fountain in Old-Geneva, with the face of a spewing neo-classical 'Greenman', then seems to have been chosen as the favourite* motif, as shown by the different enlargements made, the image selected for all subsequent 'Bruce Nauman' works. According to DS and Ref.(21.) an underlying theme of a number of projects—actual and planned—was 'Water' "inspired by a conversation between Stephen and Leopold Bloom in Joyce's 'Ulysses' on the virtues of water", and so the fountain piece would have fitted in well.

605 Portrait of Bruce Nauman, Brian Lane (c.1978) **Undistributed edition of 10 of a photograph of a fountain with BL's 'Bruce Nauman' plaque, laid into shallow cardboard box, 152x102x10; all details of publication printed inside lower part of this box, (lid of box is missing).** *Ten copies of the photo and 12 of the printed, lower part of the box (with already cut and scored flaps) found in boxes together with spare copies of other BL publications.*

606 Portrait of Bruce Nauman, Brian Lane (c.1978) **Printed folder, 258x212, enclosing**

enlarged photo of fountain with BL's 'Bruce Nauman' plaque, (planned) edition of 10, the photographs numbered (image identical to entry above). Seven prints of the photograph, Nos. 4/10 to 10/10, were found in ringbinder files leaving just Nos. 1/10 to 3/10 unaccounted for: presumably these were given to friends.

607 Portrait of Bruce Nauman, Brian Lane (c.1978) **Even larger photograph (of same image as previous two entries) mounted on card (ready for framing), 298x210, edition of 5, signed and numbered.** *All copies but No. 5/5 were found in a ringbinder. The fifth print in fact was sent to Bruce Nauman (source: a BL letter to Michael Lumb): BL would have been aware of potential copyright and legal problems and would have hoped to get the clearance for his works from BN himself. However no response from BN was found in the files.*

SOME RUBBERSTAMPED BOOKWORKS

Found among Brian Lane's files was a group of works from 1979 in which the common element is the extensive use of rubberstamps a method of printing used occasionally only by BL prior to this. These rubberstamp works are on just two subjects: 'Endangered Nature' and 'The Great War 1914–1918'. The rubberstamped bookworks are now in the Tate Gallery Archive.

ENDANGERED NATURE

701 (Untitled) Box containing Rubberstamped Cards of Wild Animals (c.1979). Prototype for a Game of 'Endangered Wild Animals' in cardboard box. Both lid and bottom of box carefully covered, inside and out, in fake 'snakeskin' paper. **Card box, 186x223x13, with two-compartments: the narrow one**

with a pencil, in the other 19 cards, 148x210, rubberstamped in four colours. *Each card stamped with a different group of six animals from the set of eight rubberstamps used; eight of the cards also have a leafy green tree. Only two animals on each card are in colour: one in blue, the other in red, but each of the animals stamped sometimes in red, sometimes in blue. Clearly the images and colours on the cards do not occur randomly, but reflect the rules of a game. But as there are no instructions, it is impossible to decipher the Game Plan. Two other pieces laid into the box may or may not have been designed for the same game:*

702 Untitled / (Endangered Species) (c.1979) **Two folded pieces of paper, 106x148, printed text with illustrations, photocopied.** *The wild animals illustrated are reduced-scale pho-*

tocopies of the above rubberstamps; the text describes the status of each of the eight animals as an endangered species. A prototype clearly but for what exactly? Just as an enclosure for the boxed Game?

703 The Elton John Award for Wildlife Conservation (c.1979) **Dummy of a folded 'Award Certificate' in a dummy of a protective sleeve, 152x102.** *Graphic design of certificate, pencilled, at the top and bottom respectively: "Big Game Hunt. Elton John Award for Wildlife Conservation"*
Name .... Score ......"
Enclosed in the sleeve a photocopy of a small newspaper photograph of Elton John putting on a fur coat, striped black and white, captioned "Super Civet. Elton looks up to scratch in this super £1150 civet jacket." The 'Score' to be filled in is consistent with the suggestion that this was part of a design for a boxed game. Why was the game never realized? As a one-off work in response to Elton John's sartorial crassness it would would have been defendable but the unauthorized use of Elton's name for an editioned game might have brought problems. The wild animal stamps made one more appearance in 'Nature is Life—Save It !', a small booklet, 1979, a feeble work by BL's standards, but the only dated use of the stamps.

THE GREAT WAR 1914–1918

704 Percussion, Brian Lane, 1979.
Manuscript of a 'musical' score, 16pp, in an olive-coloured folder, 313x250. Three pages rubberstamped in up to four colours, the accompanying text handwritten in ink.
p9. "Note 1: Text from Leon Wolff's 'In Flanders Fields' (Pan Books London 1959)"
p11. "Note 2: There is exhibited in the Imperial War Museum, London, a panel of pressed flowers the first to grow on Flanders fields after World War One."
"... and there were shells that screamed / shells that hissed / gas shells that exploded with a simpering pop / shells that whistled / and shells that wobbled across heaven rattling like a snare drum. / Finally there was drumfire reserved for special occasions. / When all the instruments blended into one homogeneous mass of sound / of such intensity as cannot be described / all bursting into jagged fragments of hot metal / that slammed into the bodies of men and mules with familiar results"
Images of bursting shells are rubberstamped on staves of musical notepaper like a musical score, but with the added excitement of watching a firework. Just two rubberstamps are used to visualize the exploding shells: an inner 'spikey' burst and a larger, concentric one of rapidly expanding clouds. Final additions to the shell bursts made by hand in a fine, red pen. The spikey rubberstamp was used also in the booklet 'Nature is Life', 1979; the expanding cloud stamp had been used previously in 'Notes on Umpiring and Exercises', 1978.

705 In Memory of the Fallen Paschendaele, Brian Lane, 1979. **Manuscript—"First Draft" —of a 'musical' score, 8pp, 313x247, (no cover or folder); title page and one completed page of the score with twelve staves: staves of a handwritten musical score alternate with a rubberstamped 'score' of densely packed, fallen, infantry men printed in red and blue ink.** *There are just two rubberstamps depicting the fallen men: one shows a prone figure, always printed in red, and the other a figure on his back, always in blue; the red figures are always lying head left, the blue ones head right.*

706 (Untitled) **Paschendaele File, together with 500 Paschendaele Score Sheets in a 'Croxley Script' Box. Untitled pale-green wallet file containing small handwritten note and sixty A4 sheets of a rubberstamped musical score titled 'Retreat' and numbered 501 to 560. (A blue 'Croxley Script' box contains Nos.1 to 500 of the same.)** *The small note has two quotations from First World War history books, one of which reads: ...*

"sometimes known as Paschendaele, after its terminal battle near the village of that name, which cost the attacking side some 400,000 casualties and achieved no results of even momentary importance. ('The Fall of the Dynasties', Edmund Taylor, Weidenfeld & Nicholson)"

This large print run differs from the 'First Draft' above in a number of details: a printed title to the score: "39. Retreat" whereas the 'Draft' was untitled; A4 sheets with four staves only of musical notes vs. six on the 'Draft'; a rearranged musical score; the musical score—only—is printed offset and on a somewhat reduced scale; the fallen infantry men are printed on the white margin between staves; the A4 sheets are numbered top r.h.corner, this must have been done right at the end, as the full sequential run to 560 is without a single, less-than-perfect copy. But the real surprise revealed only after close inspection of the printed sheets, is that every sheet is rubberstamped by hand with between 44 and 52 fallen men; every sheet is unique: there is no regular pattern to the rubber-stamped figures. This suggests the total number of hand-stampings to have been at least 25,000! The two rubberstamps have not been used in any other known publication of BL. Even allowing for BL's fascination with the subject of death, some questions remain: Why such a large print run? Was the 'edition' produced for a planned special event or occasion? And why was the project mothballed / abandoned at this advanced stage?

SOME UNIQUE OBJECTS AND BOOKWORKS

801 The sky is at least as blue as it is sky, Brian Lane (c.1968) **Banner, text on piece of cloth c.7'x 1'; printed in large letters in blue poster paint.** A leaflet with the same text was produced for the 'Fluxus Leaflet Concert' 1968.

802 The Bundle and the Boxes, Brian Lane and Maurene Sandoe (1970) **Handmade white box in Astralux, 65x183x45, titled on lid; brown card box for protection. Four deep compartments in box painted red, yellow, blue and green respectively, small foil-wrapped object in one, finely squared acetate screens as lids to each compartment.** Related to the four-day event of same name at the London New Arts Laboratory, 1970: "A sculptural piece created by BL in response to the U.N. 'Report on Slavery' of 1963 which was used as an introduction on each of the four days followed by a colour report—Red / Yellow / Green / Blue—relative to the movement of the bundle through the boxes." According to Maurene Tingey the making of prototypes like this was typical of their work and collaborations at that time: exploring themes and ideas in different formats. This object appears to have remained unique.

803 Rainbows for D, Brian Lane (c.1976) **Labelled card box containing a dozen multi-coloured cloth cones, c.270x200 folded flat, and a small white Astralux cube, 40x40x40, neatly labelled 'Rainbow (for Dee)' containing ten paper cones handcoloured by crayons in rainbow stripes.** All parts unfaded and in mint condition. Looks related to various land art projects in the Lumb Lane files, and there are photos of similar (but faded) cones in a field, but exact context of this object remains to be discovered. (A young woman named "Dee" is mentioned once or twice in BL's letters to Michael Lumb).

804 Diary, Brian Lane, Geneva, January to April 1977. Small pocket diary recording his artistic projects during his Geneva period written to keep Debbie Squires informed of progress in between her visits to Geneva. Has references to many projects described elsewhere in these papers. In the collection of Debbie Squires.

805 Bottled Cloud, Brian Lane, 1977. **Small clear glass bottle, 62 mm high, with hand-written label, in adapted wooden cigar box.** "'Bottled Cloud'. Taken from Aiguille du Midi, France." *According to Debbie Squires the idea was to release the bottled cloud in Scotland (though this was never realized). Reference to this work also in 'Diary' above.*

806 Faded–Flower Water, n.d. **Labelled set of 17 tiny test tubes with rubber stoppers and water in handmade display/storage box with room for 20 tubes.** *Description of the samples taken not kept with this set, but Michael Lumb suggests the samples were of water that had had flowers in—as the title says.*

807 Dem ol' Roumanian Blues, Brian Lane, 1978. **130x180. Two cards, one misprinted, issued by Players Cigarettes in 1936.** *Shown in 'fo(u)ndlings' exhibition at Coracle Press Gallery, 1978, and described on one of the lost-property-office 'tags' of the catalogue.*

808 A Book of Wallflowers, Brian Lane, 1980. Unique bookwork made for 'On Loan' exhibition at Coracle Press Gallery, London, 1980. Description on one of the catalogue's library-style lending cards: **"Being the successive layers of wall and ceiling papers lifted from an abandoned cottage at Devil's Bridge, Wales, October 1980." 30pp, 140x220.** *In the collection of Debbie Squires.*

NATURE STUDY NOTES

809 Clouds of Pollen, Brian Lane, Vienna, July 1982. **Bookwork in hard-cover folio, 369x257, with ties on r.h.s. Single sheet of handmade paper with yellow pollen stains, label as on folio.**

810 Tales from the Vienna Woods, Brian Lane, Vienna, August 1982. **Bookwork in hard-cover folio, 186x255, with side ties. Thirteen rubbings of tree barks on sheets of musical notepaper with six staves.** *The editioned version of this was published 1982.*

SOURCES AND REFERENCES FOR A BRIAN LANE BIBLIOGRAPHY

All sources and references listed are from the Brian Lane papers in the Tate Gallery Archive, except for 16., 17. and 25. below, of which there are copies in the collection of John Janssen. Letters are by or to BL unless described otherwise.

1. Project 67 'Books', Gallery Number Ten, London SE3, (1967)
Project 67 was the first publishing imprint used by Gallery Number Ten. Brian Lane editor; Trevor Wells associate editor. **List/catalogue, two single-sided A4 sheets in two colours (red and brown), introduction to project, and list of items published to date.** "All cheques and money orders made payable to 'Brian Lane'." "In Preparation": a two volume collection of 'Japanese Visual Poetry', (but never realized).

2. Project 67, 'Printed Objects', Gallery Number Ten, London SE3, (1967)
Companion list/catalogue to list above, single-sided A4 sheet in two colours (red and brown); introductory statement, with invitation to subscribe and list of items published to date. "All cheques and money orders made payable to 'Brian Lane".

3. Probable Latitude 76° 15' Longitude 113° 10'E London SE3 1970
"The new name derived from H.P. Lovecraft's 'At the Mountains of Madness'." **List/catalogue, two single-sided sheets printed in black (one with illustrative text), 255x204.** Proposal ('February 1970') and Statement (of the principle behind the works): "... many forms of printing and construction, two- and three-dimensional", with list of items "in the

first series"; "Please make cheques payable to 'Brian Lane". *The coordinates are those of a location in Northern Siberia. Maurene Tingey suggests some reference also to local artist Mark Boyle, who would stick pins into maps to determine the exact location of the squares of ground he would then replicate.*

4. Probable Latitude 76° 15' Longitude 113° 10'E, London SE3, 1970
List/catalogue, single-sided A4 sheet, printed in black with blue underlining. 'Second Series of Publications, March 1970'; also Gallery Number Ten reprints "reprinted from the Winter 1967 catalogue"; the latter list (n.s. / not in Archive) contains one title not listed before.

5. Probable Latitude 76° 15' Longitude 113° 10'E, London SE3, (c.1970)
Prototype catalogue, 56pp, 202x126, single-sided, with pasted-in, typed texts. Records Gallery Number Ten's live events, exhibitions, lectures and publications 1966–70, with original photos by M.Sandoe, incl. of two- and three dimensional 'publications' (dummy still incomplete, and almost certainly never realized as edition).

6. Gemma Three First Series Welling Kent (1971)
(New imprint launched by M.Sandoe following the closure of Gallery Number Ten in late-1970) **List/catalogue, two single-sided A4 sheets in two colours (red and black).** Reprints February 1970 statement of Probable Latitude ... catalogue, lists seven reprints from that earlier list, plus three new publications as Gemma Three. "Please make cheques/money orders payable to Maurene Sandoe". (No further publications were to follow.)

7. 'Publishing Project 1978–1979. An Open Letter.' Brian Lane, London SE5, August 1978.
Single-sided A4 sheet with printed text. Brief history of BL's publications since 1967 ending in statement of his belief that now is an opportune moment to resume producing

artist's publications, and inviting new contributions for three main projects for 1978–9: Artists Cards and Leaflets From Japan, ditto From Eastern Europe and The Polemic of Feminism. *From their correspondence with BL it appears that Printed Matter (N.Y.) were sufficiently impressed to mention that they had pinned the Open Letter to their Notice Board.*

8. 'Brian Lane Printed Works 1978', 162 Wyndham Road, London SE5, Jan.1979
Printed catalogue, 146x105, 16pp, stapled, grey paper covers with cut-out window. With introductory note and many b&w illustrations—undoubtedly BL's finest catalogue—lists all publications produced "during the year January 1978 to January 1979". Order Form lists 14 titles (counting the 'Information Series One' as one title); "In Preparation": 'Six Portraits of The Artist' 1978 (already with illustration) and Numbers Three and Four of 'The Fog Log Collection'; (none of these were to be published).

9. (Untitled) distribution list for 'Information Series One', (1978/79)
Two handwritten, single-sided sheets of squared A4 paper listing in tabular form the recipients (by name and address) of the numbered editions (1–50) of each issue (Nos.1–12), with numerous crossings-out and revisions by BL in different colours.

10. (Untitled) catalogue of work and activities 1966–1978, (Brian Lane) (c.1979)
Typescript of 59 numbered pages (two pages numbered '55'), introduces and catalogues all publications ephemera and other archival material (letters etc.) relating to BL's wide-ranging artistic and publishing activities from 1966 to 1978, including itemization of contents of c.50 document wallets on other artists and poets BL had collaborated or corresponded with (publications original artwork miscellaneous documents); four new publications since 'Printed Works 1978' include 'Manifesto 1' photograph album; also lists 'Small Editions

Geneva 1976': five titles not listed elsewhere (n.s./ex BLA). (Catalogue probably produced in response to enquiries post the 1978 'burst' from serious collectors/archives about earlier activities and lists / availability of earlier/missing publications).

11. 'Artists' Printed Books 1978 1980' & 'In Preparation 1980', January 1980
Prototype for new list/catalogue, two handwritten, landscape-format, single-sided A4 sheets, revised version of Introductory Note from 'Printed Works 1978' catalogue, tabulation of all publications by title, author, format, printing method, edition size and price; 'Six Portraits of The Artist' now among the published titles (but prematurely); new titles include the 'Little Xerox Books', Nos.1 and 2, Steve Wheatley's 'Stamps of Many Lands' in three formats and '69/70 for 79/80', a clutch of nine boxed reprints from 1969–70, but 'Information Series One', Numbers 11 and 12, have still to appear. Titles "In Preparation 1980" include Peter Mayer's 'Kilroy Was Here' (which did appear—the copy in the Archive the only one ever seen by the compiler— though never listed again), and Ken Saville's intriguing photo album 'Irrigation Ditch Women'.

12. 'Artist Books', Brian Lane, London SE5, June 1981
Printed list/catalogue, double sided A4 sheet, 'January 1980' crossed-out 'June 1981', handwritten revisions to newer titles, page 2, pasted over to leave original text faintly readable, and suggesting slightly later date to start with than handwritten version above. (List found clipped to Printed Matter N.Y. file, for whom it was probably prepared). 'Six Portraits of The Artists' listed as apparently published, but no editioned copy has been discovered to date, despite part-printed prototypes and full paste-ups in the files: potential copyright problems (27. below) may have finally scuppered the edition.

Newest titles are 'Little Xerox Books', Nos.3 and 4, and a set of three booklets by Jiri Valoch. "In Preparation": 'World Album of Artists Stamps', edited by Steve Wheatley and BL, (which was to be abandoned later—at a late stage.)
(No further mention, alas, of 'Irrigation Ditch Women'—despite two near-perfect dummies: did Ken Saville object to BL having 'ditched ' his (i.e.Ken's) poems along the way?)

13. "1978–82" and "Early Books", (Brian Lane), (c.1985/86 (?))
Stock list, two handwritten, landscape-formated, single-sided A4 sheets, listing by title and date of publication no. of copies by: Private, Personal, Shop, C.C. (sic), (but this cannot be a complete list of titles in-print then by any means); dates of some (mostly later) titles written as 198-(sic), i.e. not obvious even to publisher (!); only a few new items not previously listed: 'A Manual of Arms', and two postcards by Gabor Toth and Ruth Wolf-Rehfeld (both dated '1979' on card). (List possibly compiled during BL's period with the Coracle bookshop at Whitechapel Gallery).

14. 'Doctor Death Ice White and the Black Circus' Windsor 1981
68pp, 210x150, plastic spine. Catalogue of BL's 'commercial' venture with very diverse range of productions. The only BL catalogue ever to list his button badge works: 'Battle Dress': "Three sets (of different images) so far available" (one set illustrated), (though more sets did appear subsequently; most of these are in the Tate Gallery Archive).

15. 'A Selection of Books for the Frankfurter Kunstverein', Simon Cutts, August 1981
Catalogue, produced by Coracle Press, 162x124, 8pp, paper covers, stapled; Editions Brian Lane was one of the group of small presses selected for this exhibition; the six titles chosen—all of them recent productions—include a folder of silkscreen prints 'If You Go Down in the Woods', 1981—not list-

ed elsewhere / n.s.—and two of BL's button badge works ("publications made to be worn by their 'readers'"): 'Battle Dress' and 'Family Album' (the latter not listed elsewhere and not in Archive).

16. 'Printed Matter Catalog 1981 Books by Artists', Printed Matter Inc, N.Y., 1981 267x208, 160pp, perfect-bound paper covers with photographic image in full colour, (arguably the finest commercial catalogue of artists publications ever produced), p83: lists and describes 11 titles from Editions Brian Lane (one illustrated); with this P.M. became BL's most important sales outlet (together with sales via Coracle Press); clearly P.M. very much liked BL's work and continued to cajole him in the face of BL's often rather casual attitude to all matters of business, such as (not) responding to letters and orders, and (not) keeping proper records of despatches or accounts.

17. 'Printed Matter Catalog 1983/84 Books by Artists', Printed Matter Inc, N.Y., 1983/84 267x208, 160pp, perfect-bound, paper covers in two colours, p86: again lists and describes (the same) 11 titles from Editions Brian Lane. (Very few new titles had appeared since P.M. had made their initial selection in 1980/81.)

18. Letter from Hanns Sohm, Markgroeningen, Germany, 25.10.1980 Sends list of BL publications already in 'archiv sohm'—a very impressive list indeed—(and useful here in view of the sometimes conflicting evidence of what actually was published) asking BL to identify missing titles with a view to filling any gaps in 'archiv sohm'. (Again BL was very slow to respond, only—many months later—to most charmingly apologize.)

19. Letter to Michael Lumb, Henley, nr. Ipswich, 5.12.1978 Explains at some length his guiding philosophy in publishing, along the way answering more detailed questions as to edition sizes, 'specials'. Free Issues vs. sales, survival and break-

even; generally a spirit of generosity seems to prevail over conventional business principles / practice: rather than "creating (work) with the intention of financial gain" he prefers "to construct for oneself a condition in which selling is the happy by-product of a larger principle".

20. Letter to Jean Brown, (archivist), The Tyringham Institute, Massachusetts, 6.11.1978 "... even my own reference set is incomplete, and my own considerable archive collection was sold some five years ago. However I have enclosed a list ...": the enclosed list goes back to 1967, but here runs only to two typed pages.

21. Letter to Jean Brown, The Tyringham Institute, Massachusetts, 30.4.1979 Explains context of folding card 'Ceremonies', Number One,—edition of 100 not listed elsewhere—which features the wedding photo of BL & Debbie Squires and which BL had mailed out as usual, including to JB, a few weeks earlier. Apparently there were to be more 'Ceremonies'—"two more are in production at the moment"—each time involving Debbie Squires. (No more appeared—they were to split early 1981). Charmed by just having been sent a surprise cheque from JB as a belated wedding gift (!) BL responds by sending JB another hoard of pre-1978 archival material— no mention of an invoice here—"to make your archive a little more complete". (The list of this material is extant and runs to another three typed pages.) JB in thanking him in turn replied "I am sending you some money, not enough, but when I get some more money I'll send it on. Please thrive and prosper and send me all the results."

22. Letter to Jean Brown, The Tyringham Institute, Massachusetts, 11.6.1981 Mailing out a few new items including 'Manifesto 1', edition of 25, and not sure whether he has sent her this title before BL suggests, in case she already has it, "perhaps you could find a good home with somebody else for it (it's such a small edition)".

23. Letter to Jon Hendricks, (archivist), The Silverman Collection, USA, 31.3.1987 "... the larger part of my own (archive) went to the Tate Gallery, via Sir Robert McAlpine, some dozen or so years ago ... (Of) what remains ... I put together a catalogue of sorts a few years ago excerpts from which I enclose ... As for selling the material—why not ?" (The 'catalogue of sorts' may be the 59-page type-script document of 1979, listed above).

24. Ruth and Marvin Sackner Archive of Concrete and Visual Poetry, 'A – L' only, (1981) Catalogue of Archive, loose A4 sheets, single-sided, 218pp; (sent by MS to BL with letter below). Lists just three publications from BL, and two letters from BL to John Furnival. Attached is a letter from MS to BL of 23.10.1981 apparently in reply to an approach from BL: "I would be interested in your send-ing me a listing of 'Brian Lane and His Friends'. Perhaps we can come to some agreement even if the material is largely at the extreme of Visual Poetry."

25. Ruth and Marvin Sackner Archive of Concrete and Visual Poetry, 'A–L', 'M–Z', (c.1982) Catalogue, loose A4 sheets, single-sided, 318pp & 213pp. Compared to the earlier cat-alogue this much enlarged one lists just three extra items by BL, including 'Lane, Brian, Catalog of Archive, 1981 loose sheets' and '69/70 for 79/80, 1980'. *This suggests BL had send a copy of (10.) above to the Sackners, who then duly listed it, but clearly the Sackners did-n't acquire the 'BL and His Friends' material as itemized in (10.). Almost certainly the 'new' items were gifts from BL to MS, including the broadside 'It Is The Golden Voice Of The Sun' (but this is not a known BL title—can this really be by Brian Lane ?).*

26. Small Press Review, Vol.1 No.2, ed. Kevin McCarthy, London, Fall 1967

'A Quarterly Review of Small-Press Publications'. 56pp, 215x137; laid in loose the magazine's 'Feedback' sheets with the sell-otaped proofs. Listing of 14 titles (with full details) of Gallery Number Ten publications.

27. Il Corpo Come Linguado / La Body–art e storie simili Lea Vergine 1974 Giampaolo Prearo Editore, c.200pp, 232x169, many illustrations. *Almost certainly the book from which three of the the photos for 'Six Portraits of The Artist' were taken. (The 'book-marks' are BL's).*

28. Lumb Lane untitled statement n.d. / (c.1974/1975) Statement / manifesto of a planned new long term collaboration between BL and Michael Lumb; photocopy of A4 sheet in ML's collec-tion, typewritten draft text with handwritten annotations / revisions by ML; also contains announcement of 'Information Series Four' as a first Lumb Lane collaboration and joint extension of BL's sequence of 'Information Series'.

29. Quiet Yellow Sounds on the River Red with Menace, Brian Lane, Arts Workshop, Henley, nr. Ipswich, 1975 **A4 flyer, text and graphic design, for a boxed edition of the relics of an event on the river at Great Blakenham, Suffolk, 1975, in collaboration with Annetta Crane and Michael & Janet Lumb.** *Later published by BL under the Editions Brian Lane imprint.Arts Workshop was a short-lived Arts Centre of Michael Lumb.*

30. Against the Landscape, Brian Lane, Arts Workshop, Henley, nr. Ipswich, 1976 "A sculpture on the land of Suffolk. Conceived by Brian Lane and built, erected and recorded in collaboration with Annetta Crane, Michael and Janet Lumb, May 1975 to 1976." **Printed A4 sheet with text and two photographic images.** Became the source of 'Information Series One—Number Ten', Editions Brian Lane, 1978.

31. Letter from Michael Lumb to John Janssen, 21.1.2000
Three pages of notes in response to JJ's request for checking his first version of 'Books and Bookworks of Brian Lane—A Bibliography'.

32. Letter with Notes from Maurene Tingey (Sandoe) to John Janssen, 3.5.2000
Three pages of notes on her collaboration with BL on the leaflets for the Lorca event; fifteen annotated pages from the JJ documentation, especially relating to the early years (performances / events and publications, including Gemma Three).

33. BL's List of Boxes Kept In Storage
BL's handwritten lists of contents of boxes put into storage, mostly during the mid-80s. Six sheets of squared A4, various colours of ink, pencil and biro, underlinings etc; broad contents of numbered boxes containing books, papers and personal possessions; primary list of 78 boxes, and supplementary list of about 24 more boxes stored separately.

34. The Funeral of Brian Lane, 5th November 1999.
Handout: folded A5 sheet with photograph of BL, proceedings, short texts by BL, and a brief tribute: 'Brian: A Quixotic Journey'.

35. *Obituaries of Brian Lane, December 1999*
'The Guide,' Blackheath, the 'Catford and Hither Green Newsreel' and the 'Newsshopper'; also (unpublished) obituary by Simon Cutts for 'The Independent'.

NOTATIONS AND ABBREVIATIONS

Publication details shown were either taken from the publication itself—wherever possible—or from one or more of the listed 'Sources and References':
n.s. (10.)= not seen by compiler details taken from Reference No.10.
'Not listed elsewhere':= not listed in any of this bibliography's 'Sources and References'.

Date of publication:
1978= date as given in publication.
(1978)= date of publication known or derived from other sources.
(c.1978)= approximate date of publication only.
n.d.= no date.

Measurements in mm height before width.

Abbreviations:
lp= letterpress.
st= stapled.
cb= casebound.
ed.150 = edition of 150 (numbered only if stated).

Numbering of works:
001–099
Fluxus and Experimental Music 1968–1970.
101–199
Books and Printed Works 1966–1971.
201–299
Books and Printed Works 1976–1977.
301–399
Books and Printed Works 1978–1986.
401–499
Doctor Death Ice White and The Black Circus.
501–599
Information Series and Index Card Works.
601–699
Some Works in Homage of Bruce Nauman.
701–799
Some Rubberstamped Bookworks.
801–899
Some Unique Objects and Bookworks.
1.–100.
Some Sources and References for a Bibliography of BL.

COMPILED AND ANNOTATED BY COLIN SACKETT

A SELECTION OF ILLUSTRATIONS OF PERFORMED AND PRINTED WORKS

*Within the following section of illustrations the three-figure numbers in bold type (**000**) refer to an entry in the Bibliography.*

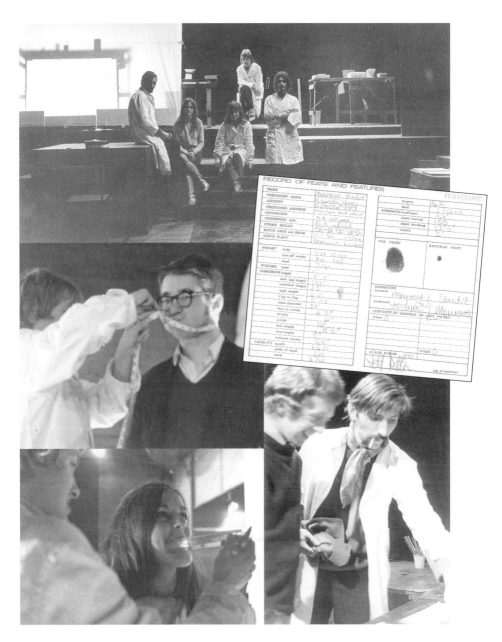

'**Fluxclinic**', performed by Brian Lane (below right, with cigarette), Maureen Sandoe and others, at Oval House, London, 15th November 1968.

INSET: Maureen Sandoe's *Record of Feats and Features*.

Publications from Gallery Ten, Probable Latitude and Gemma Three

ABOVE: Luigi Ferro, *poemi concreti*, announcement card (**114**); Kitasono Katue, *Four Portraits of a Poet*, three-fold concertina in a cover (**128**); James Mackenzie, *Les Baigneurs Sont Tous Partis*, fold-out poem in a cover (**143**).

Ladislav Nebesky, *Triangles*, cards in a wallet (**175**)

RIGHT: Nicholas Zurbrugg, *Seascape*, folding card (**158**)

MAIN PICTURE

The Fluxus Leaflet Concert

"Dedicated to 'Fluxus in general and to Ken Friedman and Ben Vautier in particular'."
First performed in November 1968 at the Aberystwyth Arts Festival and later revised for the Great Georges Project, Liverpool, in May 1970, from which this set survives. (**013–056**)

PLAY BEETHOVEN ON
PIANO

(IT'S HIS ---

h-up Number Two

NOW PLAY SOME DRUMS

This is yo---
It needs o---
authentic only---

FREE !! C.I. DANCE TICKET

peice
---rised FLUXmasterpiece
---paper in appropriate

---ady been --- t and
--- on --- ng

OMES AT

FLUXpin-up

C.I. DANCE TICKET

CAUTION

put on your hats, throw your
streamers and dance

BUILD SOMETHING
BIG

WAR GAME
The pictures you are about to see are
silent. You have been provided with the
materials to make a sound track.

FLUXUS bids you fight well.

s, hopes you w---

YOUR
COLOUR
IS

YOUR
COLOUR
IS

THIS IS A FLUXUS LEAFLET CONCERT.

All information will be conveyed by leaflet
Obey all instructions immediately.

During the course of the concert you will
privileged to be able to create FLUXorigi
works of art of unrivalled beauty. These
FLUXapproved masterpieces and should
kept and framed.

OBEY ALL INSTRUCTIONS.
OBEY THEM IMMEDIATELY.

PLEASE MOVE INTO TH
MARKED

RED

PLEASE MOVE INTO THE AREA
MARKED

BLUE

FIRST
FLUXmasterpiece

FIRST PHONIC POEM FOR RAINBOW

your letter is

B

speak this letter aloud and repeat a
7 second intervals

THIS FLUXUS LEAFLET CONCERT IS NOW
ENDED.

PLEASE LEAVE QUIETLY AND
RESPECTFULLY.

autier

BLUE
GREEN
OW

NICHOLAS ZURBRUGG

SEASCAPE

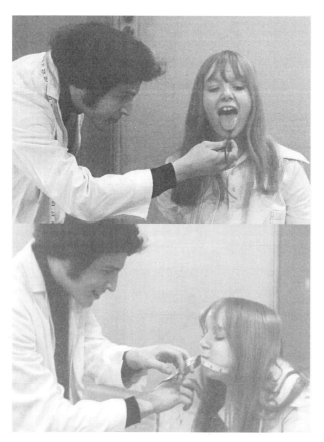

WARN THE JASMINES WITH THEIR SMALL WHITENESS

MAIN PICTURE

Red Roses for Lorca

"A quiet sort of street event" devised for Great Georges Project, Liverpool, and performed as part of the 1970 May Day procession. **(074–091)**

ABOVE LEFT: **Fluxclinic**, Liverpool, 1970.

BELOW LEFT: 'Sweets Store', Liverpool, early 1970s.
This event is described by Bill Harpe in his essay (Worlds-a-part, p.31–33) as directly resulting from the influence of Brian Lane's earlier involvement in the Great Georges Project.

MAIN PICTURE

Saturday morning, May 3 1975, Great Blakenham, Suffolk.

"Towards an understanding of the graphic images created by uniform objects floated on the surface of moving water, through the medium of an activity on the river at Great Blakenham, Suffolk. A situation created in collaboration with Annetta Crane and Michael and Janet Lumb."

See Michael Lumb's essay (Lumb Lane, p.16) along with the description of an earlier variant of this work made on the River Calder, and the adjacent canal, as part of the Hebden Bridge Festival in April 1970 (Bibliography, p.49).

RIGHT

Quiet Yellow Sounds on the River / Red with Menace (**328**).

"'Little was it dreamt when she was being built, for a herring-boat, in the Rosendal shipyard on the Hardanger, that she was to achieve this triumph, though it is hard to say what they do not dream of up there in the Fjords.' (Roald Amundsen, *The Northwest Passage*, 1908)"

Quiet Yellow Sounds on the River
Red with Menace

Brian Lane

Date __Saturday morning, May 3, 1975__
Location __Great Blakenham, Suffolk__

AGAINST THE LANDSCAPE
A sculpture on the land of Suffolk

"Conceived by Brian Lane and built, erected
and recorded in collaboration with Annetta
Crane and Michael and Janet Lumb at the
Arts Workshop, Valley Farmhouse, Henley,
Ipswich, Suffolk, during the year May 4,
1975 and May 4, 1976."

*Michael Lumb describes in detail the two
works illustrated on these pages, and the river
project on the previous pages, in his essay on
their collaborations* (Lumb Lane, p.14–16).

May 1975 | March 1976

If we for one moment forget to guard the flag, forget to fire on the flag. If it is neither protected nor attacked, it is lost for ever to a confederacy of elements having no sense of honour.

Is there honour among flags ?
Can a quiet dignity of comradeship replace the men who would gladly have died ?

It is unlikely.

Does the wind play at night ?

July 1975 | May 1976

An occurrence in the grass.

The grave no more than a grassy mound.

The tent no more significant than the remembered camp.

An overgrowth of nature.

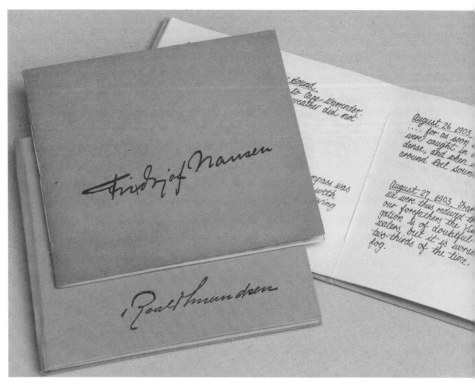

RIGHT: *Beano*
'Information Series
One—Number Twelve'
(**312**)
"Born in 1899 and
an attraction with the
Ripley Brothers
'Believe It Or Not
Show', Beano had
perfect control over
his circulation and
could stop his blood-
flow even when
purposely cut."
Printed using a silver
metallic ink, the
portrait fluctuating
positive / negative.

LEFT: The first and only two titles from *'The Fog Log Collection'*
Raold Amundsen's Fog Log (July–September 1903)
Fridtjof Nansen's Fog Log (July–September 1893) (**319–20**)
See John Bevis's essay (From Fluxus to Forensic Science, p.11–12)

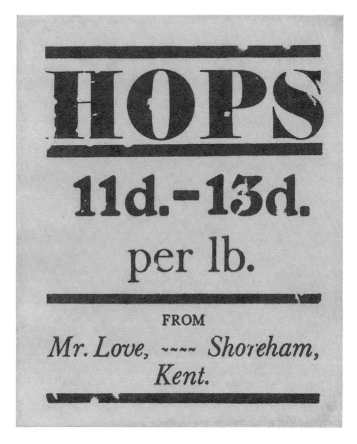

HOPS
11d.-13d.
per lb.

FROM
Mr. Love, ---- Shoreham, Kent.

ABOVE: ***Mr. Love's Hops*** *'Information Series One—Number Two'* (**302**)
"'My father inquired about the hops of Mr. Love one of the best
farmers hereabout, and a large grower, of whom several of the
villagers have what they want for growing; and he says they will be
about a shilling per pound: by about I suppose he must mean from
11 pence to 13 pence.' (1827, 'The Letters of Samuel Palmer')"
*A facsimile of a fictitious artefact—in contrast to a 'forgery'—its period
typography photocopied, and artificially aged by soaking in tea; then
dried, pressed and tipped-in to the folding card. (Illustrated actual size)*

First Post /
Last Post
(336)

BELOW: ***Granatelli In Town*** *'Information Series One—Number Three'* **(303)**
"The photographs of Andy Granatelli were taken by Maurice Rowe for an article in 'Motor' published by IBPA, July 29 1972."
The twenty-nine years that have passed since the printing of the original images has yellowed the pasted fragments of the magazine. See John Janssen's extended description of the editioning of this work, and its place in the series (Bibliography, p.66).

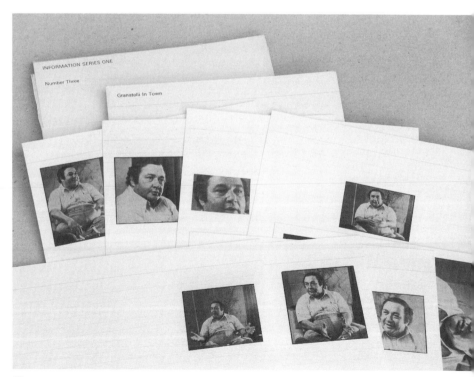

ABOVE: Steve Wheatley, *Stamps of Many Lands*
(340)
Stamps of sixteen countries: Taiwan, Nicaragua, Bahrain, Basque Provinces, China, Tunisia, Poland, Canada (actual size, *left*), Hungary (*above*), Cuba, Bhutan, Rumania, Grenada, Czechoslovakia, Bulgaria, Laos.

The set of stamps was issued in three formats: Album, Approvals Wallet and First Day Covers.

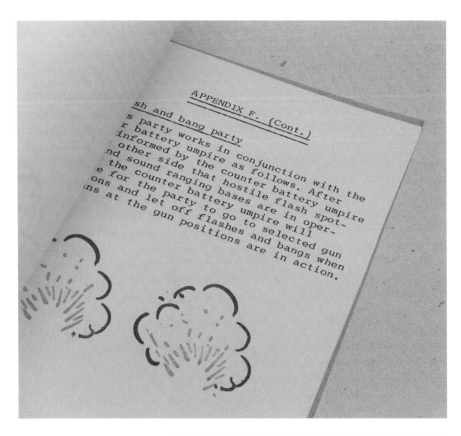

APPENDIX F. (Cont.)

...sh and bang party

...s party works in conjunction with the
...r battery umpire as follows. After
...informed by the counter battery umpire
...other side that hostile flash spot-
...nd sound ranging bases are in oper-
...e counter battery umpire will
...e for the party to go to selected gun
...ons and let off flashes and bangs when
...ns at the gun positions are in action.

ABOVE: **Notes on Umpiring and Exercises (Extracts 1)**
'Information Series One—Supplement Number Three'
(**317**)
"The texts contained in this booklet are taken from G.H.Q. Home Forces 'Standing Orders and Instructions for Exercises' 1943. The illustrations to the texts have been hand-printed from a single rubber stamp."

RIGHT: **Conventional Methods of Shewing Objects in Nature**
(**324**)

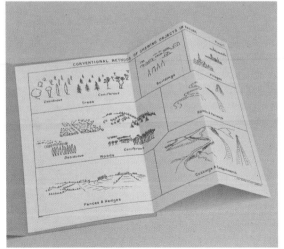

LEFT: **The Pocket Gourmet Guide to Natural History** *'Information Series One— Supplement Number One'* (**315**)

This copy—of the first twenty-five of the edition—with the eleven tipped-in illustrations hand-tinted by Debbie Squires.

Printed Works 1978

All publications illustrated on pages 90–92 and 94–95 are included in the catalogue above.

ABOVE CLOCKWISE:

Circular Displacement (**325**), *Linear Displacement* (**326**), *The Spread of Christianity in Europe* (**323**), *Bonnie and Clyde Stuff* (**327**).

IN GOOD COMPANY

Name _Terry_

Date _September 22, 1978_

Location _Coracle Press, London_

Occasion _Opening of Trevor Winkfield exhibition_

Description _Printer_

Signature _____

In Good Company (**507**)

"I have noticed a lot of name-dropping and such among artists recently. I am decided to be photographed only in good company."

IN GOOD COMPANY

Name _Brian Lane_
Date _October 22, 1977_
Location _Coracle Press, London_
Occasion _Jargon Society book-launching party_

Description _Co-ordinator of "In Good Company"_

Signature _Lane_

IN GOOD COMPANY

Name _Brian Lane_
Date _September 16, 1977_
Location _Coracle Press, London_
Occasion _Opening of Stephen Skidmore's exhibition_

Description _Co-ordinator of "In Good Company"_

Signature _Lane_

IN GOOD COMPANY

Name _Brian Lane_
Date _October 22, 1977_
Location _Coracle Press, London_
Occasion _Jargon Society book-launching party_

Description _Co-ordinator of "In Good Company"_

Signature _Lane_

IN GOOD COMPANY

Name _Brian Lane_
Date _September 16, 1977_
Location _Coracle Press, London_
Occasion _Opening of Stephen Skidmore's exhibition_

Description _Co-ordinator of "In Good Company"_

Signature _Lane_

IN GOOD COMPANY

Name _____ Brian Lane _____
Date _____ October 22, 1977 _____
Location _____ Oracle Press, London _____
Occasion _____ Jargon Society book-launching party _____

Description _____ Co-ordinators of "In Good Company" _____
_____
_____
_____

Signature _____

IN GOOD COMPANY

Name _____
Date _____ October 22, 1977 _____
Location _____ Oracle Press, London _____
Occasion _____ Jargon Society book-launching party _____

Description _____
_____
_____
_____

Signature _____

IN GOOD COMPANY

Name _____ Brian Lane _____
Date _____ October 22, 1977 _____
Location _____ Oracle Press, London _____
Occasion _____ Jargon Society book-launching party _____

Description _____ Co-ordinator of "In Good Company" _____
_____
_____
_____

Signature _____

IN GOOD COMPANY

Name _____
Date _____ October 22, 1977 _____
Location _____ Oracle Press, London _____
Occasion _____ Jargon Society book-launching party _____

Description _____
_____
_____
_____

Signature _____

IN GOOD COMPANY

Name _Brian Lane_
Date _November 11 1977_
Location _Gerald Press, London_
Occasion _Opening of Dave Morris / Diane Silcock exhibition_

Description _Co-ordinator of "In Good Company"_

Signature _____

IN GOOD COMPANY

Name _Brian Lane_
Date _November 11 1977_
Location _Gerald Press, London_
Occasion _Opening of Dave Morris / Diane Silcock exhibition_

Description _Co-ordinator of "In Good Company"_

Signature _____

IN GOOD COMPANY

Name _Brian Lane_
Date _November 11 1977_
Location _Gerald Press, London_
Occasion _Opening of Dave Morris / Diane Silcock exhibition_

Description _Co-ordinator of "In Good Company"_

Signature _____

IN GOOD COMPANY

Name _Brian Lane_
Date _November 11 1977_
Location _Gerald Press, London_
Occasion _Opening of Dave Morris / Diane Silcock exhibition_

Description _Co-ordinator of "In Good Company"_

Signature _____

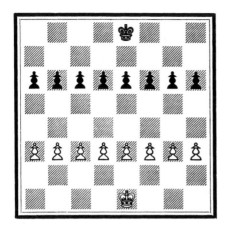
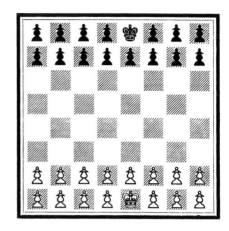
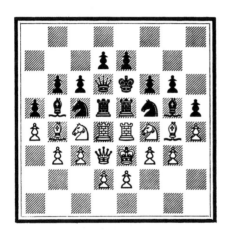
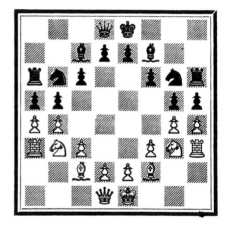

Some Improbable Openings (**329**) is composed and printed from 18pt letterpress chess 'pieces'. The dedication reads "For my father, who continues to teach me the game. And for my mother, who continues to sleep through it."

See John Bevis's description of this work (From Fluxus to Forensic Science, p.7).

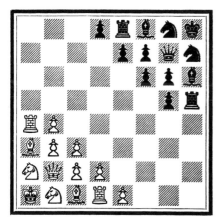
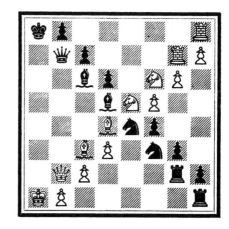
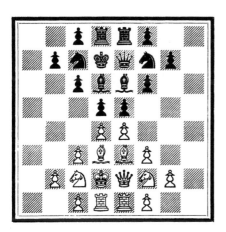

"Each set comprises 128 pieces plus Brass Border Rules. All the pieces ... are cast on em quad set of their respective bodies thus the pieces are easily interchangeable one with another when a new problem has to be set."
From Stephenson Blake printing types, *Sheffield 1969*.

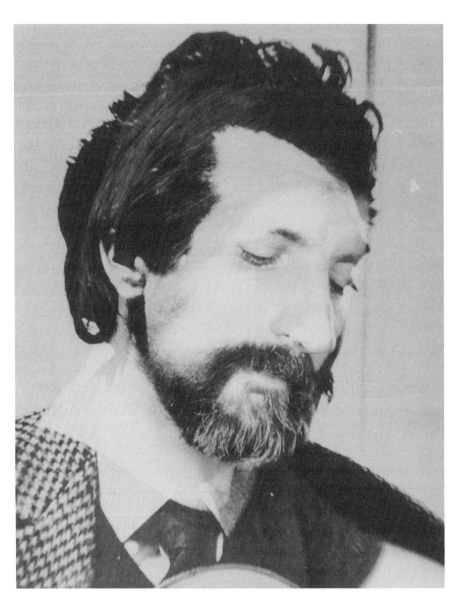

Portrait of the artist as Jesus-Rafael Soto
Source image: 'Signals' Vol.1 No.10, 1965.
Six Portraits of The Artist (**330**).
The photographs of Brian Lane by Debbie Squires.

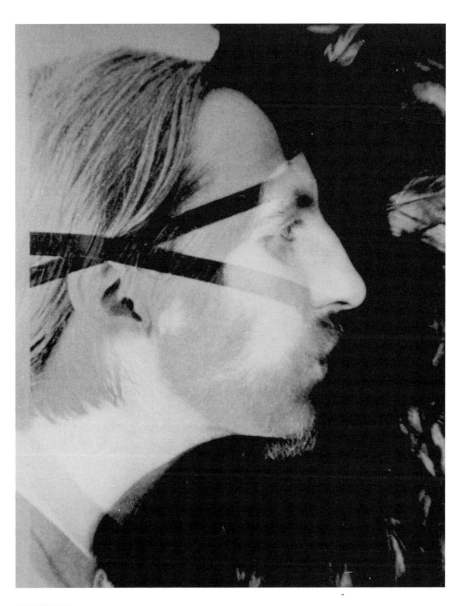

Portrait of the artist as Rebecca Horn
Source image: 'Il Corpo Come Linguaggio',
Giampaolo Prearo Editore, 1974.

Portrait of the artist as Richard Serra
Source image: 'The New Avantgarde', Pall Mall, 1972.

Portrait of the artist as Katharina Sieverding
Source image: 'Flash Art' No.38, 1973.

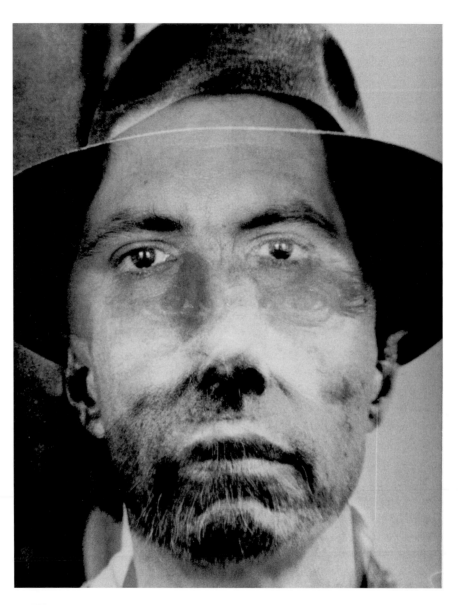

Portrait of the artist as Joseph Beuys
Source image: 'The New Avantgarde', Pall Mall, 1972.

106

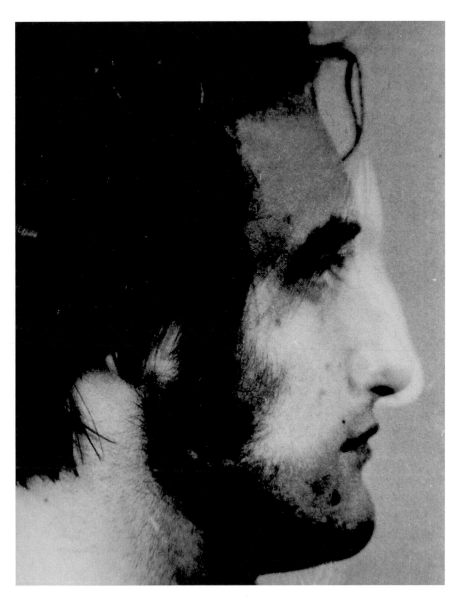

Portrait of the artist as Remo Salvadori
Source image: 'Flash Art' No.38, 1973.

When We Heard The News (**503**)

"March 4 1977. 'Lord Faulkner of Downpatrick, who as Brian Faulkner twice headed Northern Ireland governments, was killed yesterday in a hunting accident. He was thrown during a stag hunt near his home, and died almost instantly when his head struck the road and his horse fell on him.' ('The Guardian')"

See John Janssen's description of the procedures followed by Brian Lane and Debbie Squires during March and April 1977, in putting together the hundred cards that comprise this work (Bibliography, p.66).

ABOVE:

Small Flags – Geneva (504)

Alphabetically filed index cards of the names of streets in Geneva, housed in two boxes: A–L and M–Z. Two paper fragments, collected from each particular street—one by Brian Lane and one by Debbie Squires, while walking towards each other from opposite ends—are mounted (in the manner of a stamp collection) on each card.

RIGHT:

Due North of Geneva (505)

·Alphabetically filed index cards of the names of streets in Geneva. Each card with a photograph taken due north, at the point where Brian Lane and Debbie Squires met in the making of the above work.

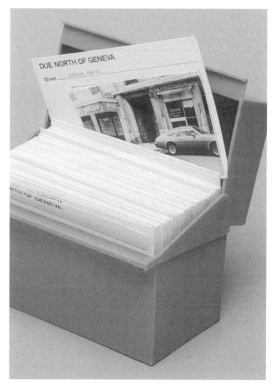

Empire Defenders (513)

Around seventy alphabetically filed index cards in a black card box. The tipped-on images following a military theme— comic-book graphics photographically enlarged and classified by subject.

Ceremonies (**338**)
"At 11.30 on March 20th 1979, Deborah Squires married Brian Lane at Camberwell Registry Office, Peckham Road, London, S.E.15."
An original photograph mounted with photo-corners in a folding card; indicated on the reverse:
"... an edition of 100 copies of Number One of an occasional series of documents".

Gary Gilmore Fan Club, Bumper Pack (**206**)

"I am increasingly disturbed by the tendency toward the 'gangster-as-hero'; the admiration in which murderers and thieves are held. Perhaps it has always been so, but it came most forcibly to me at the time of Gary Gilmore's execution. The ghoulish delight with which every move of this miserable psycho-path was eagerly relayed to millions of tv sets and equally eagerly consumed. Thousands of printed column inches. Gary had become a celebrity. I felt he should have his own T-shirt; possibly a fan-club. (letter, Brian Lane to Michael Lumb, 1977)."

No.
10028
rary
er

BELOW:

'Bruce Nauman' Plaque (**604**)

See John Janssen's description of the development of works related to Bruce Nauman (Bibliography, p.69–70); this plaque photographed attached to "a fountain in Old-Geneva, with the face of a spewing neo-classical 'Greenman'".

69/70 for 79/80 (337)

"A New Year offering in the form of a reproduction of nine works published by BL during 1969/70. Works preserve their original formats (though some have been scaled down in size) and are in a folio."

Brian Lane, *First Colour Computer*; Trevor Wells, *Twenty Four Hour Meditation Poem*; Simon Cutts, *line sails*; Thomas A. Clark, *Plucked* (below right); Kitasone Katue, *Four Portraits of a Poet*; Glyn Pursglove, *Image Chart for the Pre-Raphaelite Brotherhoood* (above right, detail); Jean-Francois Bory, *Arithmetic Texts*; Jiri Valoch, *Poem for Ad Reinhardt*; Mieko Shiomi, *Balance Poem on the Centrifugal Land*.

Image Chart for the Pre-Raphaelite E

Glyn Pursglove

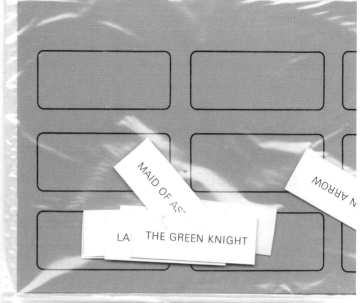

MAID OF AS

N ARROW

LA THE GREEN KNIGHT

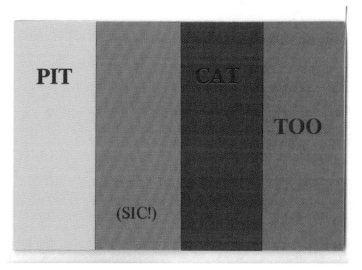

PIT

CAT

TOO

(SIC!)

DOCTOR DEATH ICE WHITE AND THE BLACK CIRCUS

From the introduction: "This Catalogue forms part of a continuing project that extends far beyond the modest aims of the present slim volume. It has its ancestry in those small country museums where, far from finding the key to all knowledge, one is captivated by the small dark corners of dusty cases where a single object sets the imagination turning for days. ... It is with all modesty that we claim that each small entry in the following pages has been carefully considered—not only for its content, but in its means of production and presentation. It is the tangible evidence of that strange museum in the recess of one person's mind; it is a portrait gallery of rogues and heroes, it is a library of documents that tell stories far beyond the paper and ink that are their fabric."

(14. in the Sources and References to the Bibliography.)

DOCTOR DEATH
ICE WHITE
AND THE
BLACK CIRCUS

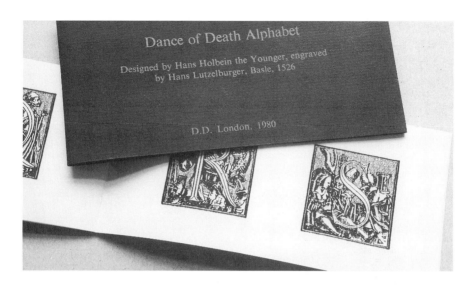

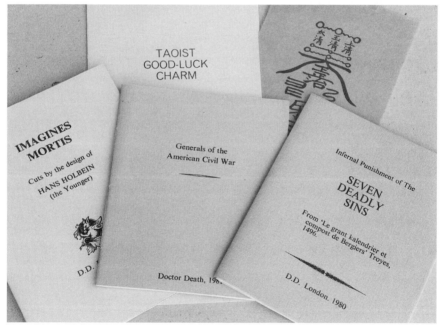

From the Doctor Death Catalogue

ABOVE: *Dance of Death Alphabet* (**413**).

BELOW: *Taoist Good-Luck Charm* (**419**); *Imagines Mortis* (**415**); *Generals of the American Civil War* (**423**); *Infernal Punishment of The Seven Deadly Sins* (**414**).

BELOW AND RIGHT:

Autograph Collections (401–403)
1—*Kings and Queens of England;*
2—*Prime Ministers of Britain;*
3—*Presidents of America.*

*Many of the publications in the 'Doctor Death' catalogue
(see previous pages) are printed with letterpress cover
designs, the text pages photocopied from typed artworks
and sewn in. (Illustrated below, 1,3,2.)*

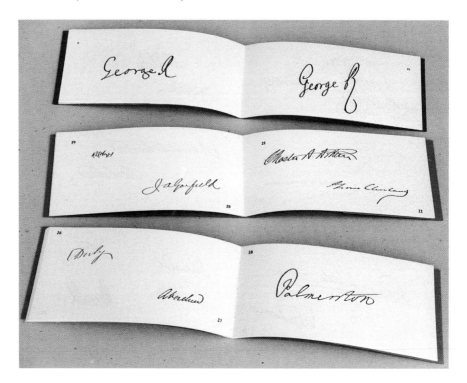

The 'Adana Eight-Five Printing Machine', used by Brian Lane until 1982.

The manufacturer's instruction manual states: *"This is the finest hand-platen printing machine in the world, with it you can print to an exceptionally high standard. Used by trade printers, schools, graphic arts departments, charities, churches, and therapy departments, it can produce one-off copies for repro masters and for proofing, and is equally suited to short or medium runs by the jobbing and home printer—for whom it remains the most popular printing press. Both card and paper can be printed, as can multi-colour work and illustrations from line and half-tone blocks. The range of work your press will print is vast—all manner of cards and stationery, envelopes, handbills, certificates, notices, menus, programmes, booklets and magazines—in fact the scope is unlimited."*

Dimensions 584x330x483, weight 15.2kg.

RIGHT:

'Battle Set'

Rubber stamps used in various publications.

BELOW:

Paschendaele Score (detail)

See John Janssen's notes on this work
(Bibliography p.71–2).
(**706**)

The Commies and Sgt.Sawyer
Seventy-one badges. (**362**)

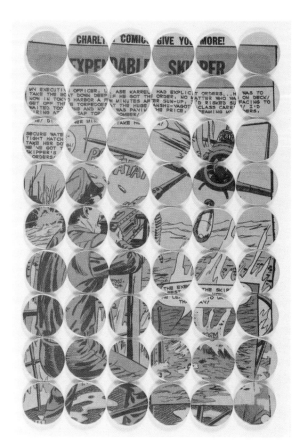

Expendable Skipper
*Fifty-four badges—two shown
below actual size.* (**363**)

OPPOSITE PAGE:

Captain Storm
Fifty-four badges. (**364**)

"... dozens of individual
badges combining to reform
into a classic page from the
early American war comics.
The whole set may be worn,
or sections of it—even single
selected badges."

Detail of a display of Fluxus material

Like the catalogue, the exhibition was put together as if to be 'read', using hundreds of original items integrated into displays of documentation and texts.

See Simon Cutts' remarks on the making of the exhibtion in his essay (Some Lacunae, p.83).

THE ARTIST PUBLISHER
A Survey by Coracle Press

*An exhibition and catalogue, below (**363**), made for the Crafts Council Gallery, London, September and October 1986.*

From the introduction BL writes: "There is an undeniably political thrust to the survey, and one whose full polemic is suggested by the title of the opening category—'Self-publishing as a Critical Alternative'. Beyond the simple insistence and continued demonstration of an economy of means of production of material that would otherwise not be seen, lies the critical stance of platforms used by artists to replace the existing, or official, means of that which already exists. Also, at times artists have published as the complete alternative to the gallery."

The Artist Publisher

The Murder Guide to London
The first of the six 'Murder Club Guides', published in 1988.

The Butchers
Published in 1991, the book that established Brian Lane as a 'true crime writer'.

Details of the crime books are in Bela Cunha's essay (The Murderologist, p.151–3).

Murder Update
"... a score or more terrifying and disturbing case histories."

Crime & Detection
In the illustrated 'Eyewitness' series.

Killer Cults
One of the last titles.

Steve Wheatley provides an in-depth investigation into Brian Lane's long-term fascination with the subject of death, in his essay (Murder, Mayhem and Brian Lane, p.34–44).

John Bevis, in the letter accompanying his essay on Brian Lane: *"... a few years ago Waterstones and the* Observer *did a survey to find the most popular book of the century. I can't remember the winner, something very predictable—*Lord of the Rings, Animal Farm, *or something. The following week the* Observer *published a 'Bottom One Hundred' of the books which had received only one vote, and Brian's* **Encyclopedia of Forensic Science** *was on the list. I still can't work out if that made it one of the least popular books of the century, one of the most obscure popular books, one of the best unpopular books, or what. And I wonder who voted for it?"*

THE ENCYCLOPEDIA OF FORENSIC SCIENCE

BRIAN LANE

Picture Acknowledgements
All photographs are by Colin Sackett, or reproduced directly from the original material, apart from the following: Tate Gallery Archive (TGA 2000/3), *pages 81, 96–99, 102–110, 121–123.* Bill Harpe, Great Georges Community Cultural Project, Liverpool, *performance images on pages 84–85.* Michael Lumb, *main picture on page 86–87, 88–89.* Simon Cutts, *Adana image on page 119.* Crafts Council Picture Library, *page 124.* Thanks are due to the publishers W H Allen, Dorling–Kindersley, Headline, Robinson Publishing; for the reproductions on *pages 126–128.*

SIMON CUTTS

SOMELACUNAEINRELATION SHIPTOBRIANLANE

Brian Lane wrote to me and thanked me "on behalf of the world" for my *Flower*, which he printed at Gallery Number Ten in 1967. It was part of his open grandiloquence, and I rarely think of him without some generous gesture, an unguarded affable politesse. His energy was formidable. I had just hitched from Nottingham and as soon as I came through the door in Blackheath, he insisted we walk through Greenwich Park and the Foot Tunnel. He knew that walking was the best form of meeting. At the end of the day we had supper in the upstairs room of Royal Parade and I can recall an almost constant stream of visitors.

The intervening years between then and the mid-seventies have become vague for me. We lost touch and Brian did one of his prolonged stints in Geneva proof-reading foreign language publications for the United Nations. In the meantime I had moved to London, and found that he lived round the corner from me in Camberwell. I had moved the treadle platten press into a space under the stairs, and I asked him to come and adjust it. There followed many printing sessions in the tight kitchen of Brymer Road, many layouts for bigger offset jobs on the table.

Then there arose the slightly absurd notion of a gallery or more public space, which was greeted with the usual humour of veiled approval inside the sarcasm of the occasion. But as soon as we started work on the dilapidated Edwardian milliners shop in Camberwell New Road, Brian was there, blow-lamp in hand. He was always there, well before me, up a ladder stripping paint.

Autumn at Coracle Press

the leaves / of burnt / paint / curl
already / the wire / wool turns / rusty

His paid job on the Information Desk at the Science Museum mysteriously ceased, and we were both signing-on in Peckham. It took six months before the gallery finally opened, and true to style, on that day Brian was back in Geneva proof-reading. His periodic return visits were always celebrated, the all-night printing sessions in the basement at Coracle, thermographing a Christmas card about snow.

He worked in earnest in these years and after on a range of his own publications and those of people near him. In those printed works of the late seventies and early eighties he espoused a socialness, an awareness of lives lived, the problems of staying alive, and a humour, that are far from the aridity of art itself.

In that time I indulged in the art scene perhaps more than Brian thought healthy, and our paths crossed intensely with the Whitechapel Bookshop which he made with John Bevis and Ian Farr under the umbrella of Coracle. Then we all worked on *The Artist Publisher*, an extended show for the Crafts Council. Although aided by John Janssen, Colin Sackett, John Bevis and David Gray, this was really Brian's show. He brought together an astounding display and analysis of the platforms artists have made for production. I still meet people whose lives where changed by that exhibition.

What I learned from him you cannot take away from me: the solidness of work, the getting down to it, the concentration on a job. Simple things, but you have to learn them somewhere. From Brian I learned that you could make an open space without calling it too much, neither gallery or bookshop, but something ambiguous, where other people could find their way to some kind of understanding. A partly domestic space, where there was always tea and refreshment, where there were always pages to fold if no-one came.

But it was the spirit of trying something, from the cynical optimism of an entrenched position. You had the feeling with Brian, working with him, that something could exist in spite of all the difficulties. That you could work anywhere with a table and chair, and with a complete unconcernedness for fame or reputation.

a smell of printing
in the kitchen from

packets of unfolded
paper wrapped in

ribbed manilla:
uncollated pages

gathered in sections
& sewn after dinner

MO TINGEY (née SANDOE)

A QUIXOTIC JOURNEY

The Printed Performance existed in embryo as a series of journeys north to wild mountainous places, made between 1963 and 1965. Brian spent many hours of meticulous planning and preparing, during which time he read extensively, writing research notes and travel details. Travelling as self-sufficiently as possible, we walked deep into remote valleys often not seeing another person for days. While I drew and painted, Brian wrote journals and derivative visually descriptive mystical stories. The travelling stopped when we moved to Blackheath Village, London in 1965, but Brian continued to use meticulous researching and planning as a working method. Later he would use these ventures as source material for two pieces of work: a proposal for *The Voyages*—a symphonic visual poem, and a three-dimensional construction with the text of a 'quartet' called *Bridges over the Sea*. Both were produced in 1971.

There was never any doubt that the shop and cellars, once acquired, would be used as a creative space. However, the move into gallery ownership was osmotic rather than planned. Initially we rented two rooms with a shared bathroom over an antique shop called 'Number Ten' and as the other tenants moved out we filtered down.

Now with space and a shop front 'Gallery Number Ten' was conceived; the acquisition of a hand-operated Adana printing press came soon afterwards. Brian and I, both coming from families of printers, had already been designing odd bits of work: hand-done lettering for signs and menus for special occasions. The gallery would need publicity material and catalogues. For a minimal outlay we could now produce our own literature as well as offering design and short-run printing services to provide some income. Our links with the printing trade ensured easy access to a cornucopia of different off-cuts of card and paper, and also to discarded fonts of type. At this time commercial printers were in the process of changing from letterpress to photo-litho reproduction; lead type, with its particular qualities, was quickly becoming redundant in the commercial world.

It was easy in London to get word around that we were looking for artists to exhibit and there was no shortage of applicants. Opening the daily post was always an exciting prospect. Early exhibitions were an eclectic mix but the choices often reflected Brian's fascination with supernatural parallel worlds as represented by authors such as Aleister Crowley, H.P. Lovecraft and with Surrealism. He had particular admiration for Salvador Dali. The criteria for selecting work focussed on integrity and experimentation—never including the potential for commercial success.

From its inception, 'Gallery Number Ten' aimed at offering a complete service to artists, by artists. This gave the advantage of retaining control over what was associated with the name. Brian put all of his dynamic energy into finding out what was innovative, that he could relate to, while building a reputation for the gallery.

The nature of the venture meant that Brian had to change his way of working from the inward turning, isolated mode of the journeys to an outgoing and collaborative approach. Adopting his new role with zeal, he soon acquired the interest of local newspapers. A short slot on the BBC evening regional news featured, I recall, the 'Fantastic Art' exhibition which probably reflected media interest in the 'Swinging London' of the mid-60s with its underground iconography favouring magical mysticism.

The need to provide a continuing flow of exhibitions ensured that Brian's delving research skills were put to use digging out all that was new and formative. But while discovering the entrepreneur within himself, he still felt unfulfilled. From our early political activities in Bexleyheath (Kent, England), we knew and admired the Red House and Brian was developing a respect for the philosophy of the artist craftsman movement of William Morris and his associates. Poetry was having a media renaissance with Christopher Logue's 'Red Bird' combining music and poetry, and Bob Cobbing intoning his verse on BBC radio. Brian began making contact with visual poets and small, contemporary artist-run presses. In a radical departure from the tenor of previous work, Brian staged an exhibition of 'Concrete Poetry' at the gallery in May 1966. The exhibition catalogue records that there were publications on show and also available for sale from Ian Hamilton Finlay's 'Wild Hawthorn Press' and John Furnival's 'Openings Press'. Also on display was original work from artists including John Furnival, Dom Sylvester Houédard, Edwin Morgan and Bob Cobbing.

Concrete poetry had connected Brian with the contemporary movements emerging in such fields as music and performance. Number Ten began to fill with what sometimes seemed like a continual stream of visiting artists. It was around this time that gallery exhibited the work of Ian Breakwell and he, his partner and his cat come to lodge with us for a few weeks while they were flat hunting. Brian said of himself "I was born ... with an insatiable curiosity as to why things are the way they are". He thrived on listening, analysing and contributing to other people's ideas and plans. There were words such as 'multiples' in the air and fired with ideas he began Gallery Number Ten publications-some of the work he selected for reproduction demonstrated Brian's growing interest in experimental combined media. Titles to his own works from this time, *Apparatus for the Observation of Miracles* and *The Seven Seals* still reflected his personal interest in mysticism.

Around this time Brian acquired 'the lad', as he was to be known. Trevor Wells lived nearby; he had left school, was unemployed and developed the habit of dropping by the gallery most days. Brian needed a close working companion. I was the gallery photographer and also fulfilling my own commissions all while studying so I become less available. Intrigued by what was going on in the gallery, Trevor was fascinated by Brian and was soon sucked into helping with the more mundane tasks. When he first appeared in the gallery he was dreamy and unmotivated-Brian set to work like Svengali. Trevor grew under this tutelage and beginning to win Brian's confidence was trusted with operating the Adana, not only as an assistant but also to develop and produce his own ideas. 'The Arrow Syndrome' exhibition was the result of collaboration between Brian and Trevor. Trevor's growing confidence was his undoing. When he took a small step too far he was 'banished'. I would like to think that Trevor found a creative niche but I fear not. Jeff came next but the chemistry was missing and eventually faded from the scene. However, for a while, the advent of Trevor had freed Brian to extend his activities.

Brian's constant creative need to push his boundaries meant he liked to work on projects with a clear beginning, middle and end. Work on the current would fire the next, always leaving him impatient to start. Brian felt restricted by the gallery; he enjoyed the private views and gradually they developed into opening events-mainly readings at this time. Once an exhibition had been planned, publicised, hung and opened, Brian had mentally finished with it and needed additional challenges. An avowed curiosity about all things coupled with an incessant need to move on and understand more was perhaps the reason that he developed Project 67. This was a 'literary-graphic' project, inviting contributions such as "poetry collections, monographic folios of graphic works, broadsheets, objects and phantasies [sic] and poster prints ... from artists and writers". It was to be produced as limited editions of printed and constructed works. Although Project 67 had a time limit imposed some additions were made later. The venture was conceived as an exhibition that could be transported and displayed in other venues in conjunction with supporting live events, giving Brian the opportunity to expand his horizons and communicate with a wider audience. The opening event of an exhibition of Project 67 publications at the Institute of Contemporary Arts (Pall Mall, London) marked a departure from the more usual emphasis on the spoken and printed word and included a performance by Adrian Nutbeem who composed conceptual electronic music. Later, Adrian worked with John Bucklow (who lived locally) and 'The Gentlemen of the Quiet Pavement' for a performance at the Queen Elizabeth Hall on London's South Bank.

Brian was experimenting with breaking out of the confines of traditional exhibition formats and wanted to concentrate more on staging events comprising the contemporary ideas of integrating performance, music, spoken and visual arts. His connections with the international scene proved crucial for this tangential change of direction. Early Gallery Number Ten publications reflected Brian's developing ideas, including work by Jean-Francois Bory and Edgardo Antonio Vigo, done in association with Contexte, Paris. The gallery exhibited the work of Luigi Ferro, introducing Brian to the electronic music movement in Italy. Crucially Brian discovered the work of the Fluxus movement of North America; he felt ideologically close with, to quote Michael Lumb, the Fluxus ideal of "an intermarriage of life and work". The work of Ken Friedman was published under the Project 67 imprint but it was performance that possessed Brian now.

The publications had run their course and Brian took a short-term proof reading contract with the United Nations in Geneva to finance the major change he was working towards. The enforced isolation he experienced in Geneva meant that he had time to build up his network of contacts. In the cause of his aims Brian was an avid and persuasive correspondent.

On returning to London, both mentally and financially refreshed, Brian planned for a series of events each consisting of a series of interlinked performances. There was a final 'outing' for Project 67 at Bristol Arts Centre in January 1968 and the imprint reached it's pre-programmed end. There was much to do; the public image of the new group had to be perfected and Rainbow Day needed to be discovered, then moulded. There were performance venues to be negotiated, participants approached, programmes agreed, props and scenery to be made or found, rehearsals held, programmes, leaflets, invitations and publicity to be designed and printed.

Brian's journey led through the interconnected routes of the printed word, experimental poetry, both visual and sound effects and electronic music; all were to be fused in a major series of collaborative performances. Already practised in staging small-scale events, we had developed a repertoire that could be utilised and built upon. The gallery by now ceased to be the stage for small scale events and exhibitions and had, by necessity, become a workshop for experimenting with effects, building scenery and producing publications for the series of performances that we were to stage in quick succession at the end of the year.

Part of my role as 'gallery photographer' was to invent ways of creating either a specific visual effect or to design and create new effects. A J-F Bory text needed to be translated into 3D for an event, the words and graphics experienced holistically becoming an environmental piece. The equipment we had access to was minimal: now it seems ante-deluvian that I took a black and white photograph of the printed text with a 35mm camera, while Brian built a person-sized box from wood fibreboard and painted it black. The image was projected into the inside corner of the box. One of our 'special effects' were slides usually made from celluloid (or other materials that smouldered well), each worked on individually with transparent coloured inks, placed into mounts and projected onto a large screen. The audience could watch the images burn as we turned off the cooling fan in the projector. Timing was crucial, too long without the fan and at the minimum we burnt out the projector bulb; if the interval before switching on the fan was too short the maximum effect of the destruction was lost. Each slide was unique and so were the performances. I remember an unusually cross Brian having to amend the staging of part of the programme a day or so before the Queen Elizabeth Hall performance; we had fallen foul of fire regulations.

Brian booked the Queen Elizabeth Hall at London's South Bank, a major venue chosen to give the new group maximum exposure and the performance needed to be rehearsed. We had outgrown the gallery as rehearsal space and access to a larger venue equipped with stage, lighting, and amplification was necessary. The Studio Theatre donated suitable space for rehearsals at the Oval (Kennington, London). The series of performances that were staged later in the year at the Studio Theatre were our thanks. Brian had always admired the 'showman' icons of a culture, people whose lives were synonymous with their work and ideas and he became increasingly concerned with his own projected personality. It was no accident that the poster for one of the 'thank you' performances at the Oval is dominated by a silhouette of Brian's head; wearing reflective sunglasses and gazing past the observer, staring through the gallery window and into the distance. The opportunity to invent Rainbow Day arose from a typographical error and was seized upon. Brian would indeed be satisfied if the exact identity of Rainbow Day remained a mystery.

This was my last year at college. I took my finals in the spring and had won a travelling scholarship from the Worshipful Company of Glaziers. The itinerary for the grand tour was planned so that it satisfied both our immediate research needs and the terms of the scholarship. We saw many of the cultural capitals of Europe and our travels took us to medieval cathedrals, modern architecture and exhibitions of modern art. Brian had always felt drawn to churches and their associations with death and the supernatural. Travelling in an old Austin A35 van called 'Beelzebub', we either slept in the back or stayed with a welcoming network of creative people. Certainly we met or lodged with J-F Bory, Julian Blaine, Jochen Gertz, Luigi Ferro and their partners and friends. In contrast to the cultural opulence of the cities we would drive to remote places to overnight in the van and would find old chapels, cemeteries and abandoned buildings, places of mystery. I photographed everything that we liked or needed to record and Brian meticulously logged the details.

Our heads were buzzing with ideas on our return to London in September 1968. Brian had used his time in Europe productively, discussing programme details with the artists and cementing a few working schedules. Now we had to concentrate on completing preparations for the QEH and the series of events at 'Pavilions in the Park' (SW London), Kennington (London) and Aberystwyth (Wales), that were to follow in quick succession. It was an intense time, leaving my memories disjointed.

The structure channelled through Brian and he negotiated the schedule so as to be the only person who knew the whole picture; he thrived on the responsibility and control. Brian only burdened people with what they needed to know and communicated this clearly. I was grateful for this as I could not have kept pace with all that he was involved with. He drew from enormous energy and was quite capable of spending "a-night-in-the-pit" (as he referred to the gallery cellars) operating the Adana press, endlessly printing without sleeping, spend the next day rehearsing and staging perhaps unrelated 'away day' events. The leaflet concerts generated huge amounts of printing, but the physical action of operating the press becomes rhythmic after a while and is quite conducive to thinking through the logistics of the many differing demands required to meet the tight and very public deadlines. As he worked the press Brian could be mentally arranging meticulous stage directions, an event or thinking through designs. The Adana operator has to stand; on a long print run a few minutes seated with a note pad and pen to make lists, record thoughts or decisions was welcome. Each series of performances had a different focus which brought with it different demands on our time. Everyone had their part to perform and it could vary from designing and making publications or scenery to script writing or performing.

It was a life that engendered creative intensity and Brian felt fulfilled, calmly directing and interconnecting the conceptual products he facilitated. Much that was then 'cutting edge' has now been watered down through time. Computers allow you to transform type, words and images, to make, compose and mix sounds or enter into a virtual reality on command. Today it is commonplace to build 'installations'—an artist who creates environments is a nominee for the 2001 Turner Prize, and schoolchildren take over a library for a day and transform the familiar environment into a fantasyland.

There was a stray event in 1969 for the 'Reigate Living Arts Workshop', otherwise after the frenetic activity of the past year it was a time of retrenchment. There was unfinished business arising from the performances that we had staged. There was the recording of events to be completed and many works that had been performed had not been followed through to their conclusion. It was time to plan for a new series of events and a related publication imprint but the costs of the last year had, as usual, outweighed any income generated. We were sinking into debt. It was an opportune time for Brian to return to Geneva for a three-month contract and we both had time to reflect, work and rework our ideas. Brian decided to call the new imprint 'Probable Latitude 76° 15' N Longitude 113° 10' E' and admitted that the name was derived from H.P. Lovecraft's *At the Mountains of Madness*. The map reference places this near the Lower Tunguska on the Central Siberian Plateau, just south of the Arctic Circle. It is probably not a coincidence that Brian was also familiar with the work of Mark Boyle who lived locally and used a randomly selected map reference as a source for his work.

Brian worked on finalising the new set of publications and the next series of events planned for the spring of 1970 and I concentrated on translating the 'Trilogy' series of performances into publications ready for the new imprint. They were planned as a contemporary manifestation of the Pollock Toy Theatres but without the traditional proscenium arch. *Boxes*, *Black into White* and *Forest* were miniature DIY kits that recreated the performance environment. There was a graphic notation to represent incidental sounds that the live performance engendered; sounds such as plastic rustling as a performer moved through it, scenery scrapping on the floor, or silence.

I was also enjoying the luxury of having a relatively long time to conceive and design a series of leaflets. Lorca's poetry is visually evocative and Brian admired him as a 'tragic' icon; his short life represented many of our 'political' ideals. Each leaflet was designed as complete so that, true to Fluxus ideals, we could shower the audience with 'art'. However, the leaflet events demanded mountains of printing and neither of us was good at compromise. Brian was more realistic about mass production than I was, probably because he did more printing, and when we came to print for the Lorca leaflet concert at the Great Georges project in Liverpool, some of the original designs had to be adapted or were produced in shorter runs. The exact colour of the paper and the ink used for each leaflet was critical and if we ran out of a particular paper from our supply of off-cuts, it was difficult to find matching paper at a price we could sustain. Brian wrote to me of his search for a specific burgundy: " ... not particularly good but a repulsive enough colour. It also has the added attraction of costing 5d for a big sheet. See what you think." Our aim was to visually evoke Lorca's description of the 'oppressed reds' and 'garnet coloured violence' of Harlem. Other leaflet designs demanded prohibitive amounts of labour and drawing inks over a long print run. White leaflet-sized blotting paper with the bottom third soaked in India ink gave a velvet black, unachievable by any other method, to evoke "My flesh and clothes are turning black like jet". An Indian tissue paper immersed in a rich yellow transparent drawing ink and dried before being printed using opaque white ink describes the texture and colour range of "I want the skull's teeth to shine and yellows to flood the silk".

'The Black and White Tea Party', devised for the 'London New Arts Laboratory' and staged there on the 21st April 1970, offered Brian the opportunity to mark Rainbow Day's sudden departure from the group. As the invitation states it is her birthday and the performance was dedicated to her, Herman de Vries and the memory of Ad Reinhardt. Brian liked ritual and perhaps the event was also in memory of the demise of 'Rainbow Day, Brian Lane and the first Dream Machine'.

Now that life was more sustainably paced, the gallery re-opened on an irregular but advertised basis with exhibitions such as Luigi Ferro's work, beginning with an electronic music event, and we were ready with masses of leaflets produced for the concert and street events at the 'Great Georges Project' run by Bill Harpe. This was, in retrospect, to be the last major outing of this particular phase of Brian's journey; he had decided to go in another direction and was planning a very different project and use for the gallery.

By placing a few small advertisements in relevant publications, Brian began to advertise for ephemera and objects associated with religious rites, death and the supernatural. As was his way, he began to make detailed records and catalogue each piece. I remember gently unpacking a dusty wooden box filled with what were purported to be the sandy bones of a dolphin that were found in the sacred river Ganges and I arrived home one day to find most of the gallery filled by a large black wooden coffin bier. The landlady gave us notice to quit soon after this, as she wanted to sell the premises and Brian and I went our separate ways. I don't know what happened to the artefacts mentioned but the subject matter was to re-emerge in 1971 as 'Black Circus Designs', albeit as slightly different manifestation of the original concept.

Incidentally, what was the gallery now comprises one half of 'The Cactus Pit', a restaurant. Blackheath Village is not the creative hub it once was.

HUGH SHRAPNEL

WORKING**WITH**BRIANLANE

I first encountered Brian Lane in the late 60s, that heady period which marked the heyday of English experimentalism in the arts and much else besides.

At that time, Brian and I were both living in Blackheath, near Greenwich in South East London. Blackheath then had the friendly, communal atmosphere of a *real* village—much less so now alas! It was full of memorable characters, including many artists, writers and musicians each going their own sweet (and sometimes not so sweet) way, seemingly answerable to no one. Blackheath Village as a whole was then a remarkable artist's centre—almost a latter-day mini version of the Paris in the early years of the last century. Among the musicians and artists I was acquainted with at the time were the painter David Williams, the photographer John Bucklow, the jazz trombonist Paul Rutherford, the avant-garde bassist and composer Barry Guy, and the saxophonist, composer and poet Bernard Living.

Life then seemed more straightforward—we just got on with things without having to look over our shoulder. This was that what seems to us now oh so remote era before the seemingly all pervading presence of market forces had had a chance to have such a deadening effect both on human life in the mass and on real individuality. So, in those now seemingly innocent and idealistic far off days in Blackheath, as elsewhere, pubs could just be pubs (not part of a chain as the former Three Tuns has been for years and now, depressingly, The Railway) artists could just be artists and shopkeepers could just be shopkeepers. The plethora of boutiques, restaurants, supermarkets and housing agents in Blackheath village today hardly allow breathing space for shops of *real* character. Who could forget the general stores run by the wonderful Madeline Moore who would never fail to impart thought-provoking philosophical advice when calling in of a Sunday morning for milk or baked beans? There was also the famed 'Three Tuns' pub run by an extraordinarily enlightened publican who, almost paternally presided over a mainly (but by no means exclusively) young and wonderfully varied albeit sometimes bizarre clientele. Although there is perhaps a danger in seeing that era through rose tinted spectacles [see 'Afterthought' below], one thing is for sure: there was a lot less cars then. If Madeline Moore were around today, you wouldn't appreciate what she had to say because you probably wouldn't be able to hear her over the din of traffic!

Brian's Gallery Number Ten was an integral part Blackheath life while at the same time being quite unique, more like an 'anti-gallery' perhaps. Before I had got to know Brian, my mother, herself a local artist, one day wandered innocently into the gallery only to be confronted with a multitude of arrows of many different sizes and colours constantly moving, wafted by the gentle breeze from the Heath, pointing in many directions, clearly indicating something, many things—but what? She said she found the experience rather disconcerting and unsettling. I was intrigued! This rather disturbingly ironic contradiction between the very precise and the random was somehow, very 'Brian'. We soon struck up a friendship.

At the time I was a very young composer (21 or 22) seeking new things in music. I had studied with that pioneering figure in music, Cornelius Cardew (very improbably in the hallowed, cloistered 19th Century surroundings of the Royal Academy of Music) and had recently joined his Scratch Orchestra. It was an exciting time in the arts; a forward-looking era full of optimism and new ideas with a healthy disdain for hallowed conventions. Many artists, musicians and writers at that time were breaking out of hitherto fixed boundaries and exploring various kinds of fusion between the arts. The Scratch Orchestra was an important example of this. It was a large pool of 'classical' and jazz musicians, non-musicians, visual artists, non-artists, anyone—all devoted to the performance of experimental music. The Scratch Orchestra was important in taking music out of the long-established concert halls and out into the communities including town halls, community centres, and remote country village halls. It is an interesting and significant fact that although Brian was not in the Scratch Orchestra, he was exploring similar areas quite independently. I remember taking part in a poetry event Brian organised, based around the poetry of Lorca, in a poor area of Liverpool. For this event Brian collaborated with Bill Harpe who ran the St George's Project, an arts project based in a very poor estate in Liverpool in which people were given the opportunity to write poetry, paint etc. Brian's Lorca event involved street leafleting in which families from the St George's Project took part.

Brian and I had a real empathy for each other; his work at the time was closely involved with music. He had a keen and perceptive interest in many kinds of music, from popular to classical, including the latest developments in contemporary music. Likewise I, a musician, had always had a very strong interest in the visual arts. I was very interested in the work and ideas of the visual artists in the Scratch Orchestra such as Psi Ellison, Dave Jackman and Tim Mitchell. Brian was a few years older than I and exerted a big influence on me at the time. In the comparatively short time (about 2 years) I knew him, I almost looked on him as an older brother. He was a complex personality, very single-minded and utterly devoted to his work. However he was also very keen to work with other artists and was an influential and leading figure in the art world; he had recently mounted the 'Rainbow Day, Brian Lane and the First Dream Machine' event at the Queen Elizabeth Hall. Despite his comparative fame he nevertheless offered to work with me, a very young and entirely unknown composer, and did the same for the jazz musician and poet Bernie Living. For this I was, and remain, very grateful. Our collaboration came about when, one day I showed Brian my 'Scratch Book'. Each member of the Scratch Orchestra was encouraged to keep a 'Scratch Book' of musical compositions, 'improvisation rites', a research project and anything else—all of which was to be looked on as potential performance material. Most member's 'Scratch Book' consisted of verbal, visual and musical material—more often miscellaneous ideas rather than fully fledged pieces—'matrices' intended for performance. These would often be theatrical 'events' or 'happenings' not directly connected with music at all; in this sense my scratch book was not untypical. However, unlike most other Scratch Orchestra members, I was rather secretive about it and only actively promoted performances of three or four of the items in the Orchestra (perhaps I did not feel the contents fitted in with what the Orchestra was doing). However, to my surprise, Brian was very enthusiastic about it and offered to print some of the material.

In the basement to Gallery Ten, Brian had a wonderful array of what would seem now in these computerised days, primitive printing equipment. What started as a straightforward project to print my material became something much more—a real collaboration between a musician and an artist (although the result doesn't fit into any clearly defined artistic category). The content of my 'Scratch Book' consisted of musical compositions (in verbal form), various quotations (from Lewis Carroll, Samuel Beckett, Magritte and others, as well as personal friends), improvisation rites, line graphics, a number score, several poems and miscellaneous thoughts and ideas. Most of the pieces had no direct relationship to music at all.

Brian selected 32 items and, through the use of various typefaces and paper, realised each one in a different way. In one Lewis Carroll item, Brian uses semi-transparent paper overlaid over card; in another piece ('Variations') the verbal 'theme' is printed on a small upright card with the single word 'variations' each printed on separate very small cards contained in a pocket attached to the main card. Somehow Brian's visual representation always seemed apposite; for instance, a rather mysterious item about the sun and moon is printed in minute type. The overall result was a visual realisation, which added a whole new dimension to the original pieces; the result—Brian's visual realisation as much as my actual pieces—amounted to considerably more than the sum of its parts. Perhaps because the overall content had a strong vocal and theatrical element, we decided, rather boldly, to call the work *Opera*; (I cannot remember whether this was my idea or Brian's). The items were loosely contained in a small plain white cardboard box with the word 'opera' printed in small capital letters on the bottom right hand corner on the top (in hindsight rather reminiscent of the Beatles' *White Album*). On the underneath of the box on the left-hand side, again in small letters was printed: by HUGH SHRAPNEL/ Designed by Brian Lane. Brian's treatment of my material is beautifully done and has great elegance.

Brian did an edition of 21 copies and got me to sign each one. He sent some copies to well-known artists and organisations although I cannot recall whom to. Our work on *Opera* was done mainly during the summer of 1970. I recall many long summer evenings at the gallery after working, discussing every idea under the sun while consuming vast quantities of wine thereafter going for rather unsteady walks over the heath in the small hours.

Looking at *Opera* again recently after nearly 30 years I was struck by how much a 'period piece' it is. This is hardly surprising. It is clearly strongly influenced by American musicians of the time involved with Fluxus such as La Monte Young (a major influence on us in the Scratch Orchestra at the time) and George Brecht (the form of *Opera* being perhaps a bit like the latter's *Water Yam*). However the general tone is whimsical, fantastic and occasionally humorous in a rather gentle way as opposed to the sometimes quite aggressive character of Fluxus (e.g. the blood curdling compositions of Nam June Paik)—English reticence on my part perhaps? It is regrettable that, to my knowledge, there has never been a performance of *Opera*.

Unfortunately by 1972 I had lost touch with Brian. This was not due to any disagreement but only that we moved in different directions. Fairly soon after I, along with Cornelius Cardew and many other musicians within the Scratch Orchestra became disillusioned with the avant-garde and sought a new content in our music—that of the struggles of the working class. Although much has happened since then, both in the art world and in the world as a whole, an attempt to find a new and more relevant content and a way out of the narrow coterie of the 'new music world' is still my major pre-occupation as a musician and composer. My experience of working with Brian was an important lesson on the road to realising this.

Afterthought

I suppose it was not *quite* as simple a picture as that. It would be naïve to suggest that 'market forces' held sway any less then than now, or were any less a negative factor in society. However, I do not think that commercial interests held such sway in the arts then. The contrived packaging of a 'Cutting Edge' new music 'scene' or a 'Sensationalist' art 'scene' was less in evidence then. Even such an outwardly banal artistic product of the 'consumer society' as Warhol nevertheless was, at the same time, an ironic comment on it; (Warhol did not need Saatchi and Saatchi, he did it himself!). Someone recently remarked on the strangely static times in which we live. This is perhaps a clue to a feeling of inertia, of *déjà vu*, in the arts today, a certain lack of real passion and conviction. Cynicism and a lack of idealism are endemic in life today overall; the arts, which are supposed to offer an energetically alternative outlook to the status quo, have become increasingly subservient to it. Artists, and everyone else, have to break away from this in order to begin building something *really* new rather than a packaged 'new'. I think that Brian's work (my knowledge of which is limited to his of the late 60s–early 70s) was a real search for new things and experiences in art, music and theatre.

SUSAN DUNKLEY

MYTIMEWITHBRIANLANE

The ad in *Time Out* said: "Arts/Crafts oriented lady, with an appreciation of the bizarre. needed to help steer new project to wealthdom—Box No 615"—I'm looking at it as I type this now—a crumpled piece of yellowed newsprint kept all these years with some of the scores of love letters, cards, poems, jokes, artworks, photographs and messages from Brian over the thirteen years that we were together.

But the *Time Out* ad was the very start of it all … I'd just returned to London after five years in Australia and a year in Cornwall and I was bored, lonely and restless. The ad maybe offered a door ajar to new possibilities and I sent a suitably bizarre letter to Box No 615. By return, I received a bulky package, addressed in beautiful rounded handwriting. Inside—the first manifestation of the contradiction that was Brian Lane—a charming, complimentary letter and a horrendous catalogue bearing an image of 'Doctor Death' and offering the reader reproductions of the blood-stained letters of Jack the Ripper, scale models of the guillotine (fully working), tapes of Charles Manson as a rock singer and worse—or better if you prefer.

Brian's letter informed me that the eye-patched, toothless madman on the cover of the catalogue was in fact himself—but considerable cosmetic cunning has been employed. I replied immediately—what woman in her right senses wouldn't.

The correspondence flowed between us and a few weeks later my doormat yielded up a beautifully hand-printed invitation to "luncheon with Doctor Death" Still no spoken word had passed between us—and I strode forth to meet a man who looked like a vampire, sold death and destruction and lived over a junk shop in South East London—an area totally unknown to me—foolhardy perhaps—but these were less paranoid times. Brian had sent instructions—ring the doorbell and wait—it could take a while for anyone to appear. Finding the doorbell was not easy and attention was easily diverted by the huge stuffed bear and headless dummies in the fly-blown window of the junk shop below the flat. I rang the bell—ready to run—and waited. Eventually the sound of footsteps on bare boards became audible—by now my heart was a painful tom-tom accompaniment to my terror (not helped by half a bottle of Dry Vermouth—Dutch courage of the early '80s). The door slowly opened and there stood Brian Lane—soft brown eyes, smartly trimmed beard, jeans, M&S shirt, and a totally charming smile, "How nice, and how brave, of you to come" he said, "You see I really don't look too much like the catalogue cover, I hope—let's have lunch".

We picked our way through the curiosities of the dusty junk shop and up the stairs into the three floors of total fascination that were Brian's living and working place. Every inch of every wall bore something that made you want to stop and ask. There was a dark-room, a printing press room, shelves and shelves and piles of books, files, papers,—all in military order—and—a bath in the kitchen and a lavatory in the back yard. It was indeed a different world to me. And I definitely wanted to explore it.

I knew practically nothing about the contemporary visual arts—in those days before Saatchi and the YBA's and the Turner Prize and all the hype, avant garde art to most people was an incomprehensible pile of bricks in the Tate and people who rode bikes over canvases for no reason anyone could quite put their finger on. Brian was, above all things, a wonderful teacher, an enthuser and an imagination-stroker of the finest degree; he had just found himself in me a blank canvas, unprimed and ready to soak up all the information he so ardently adored to impart. It was, in a way, love at first sight

I stayed for lunch—and dinner—and breakfast—popped home for a change of clothing and to make a cameo appearance at the Royal College of Music where I was supposed to be working—and three weeks later I moved in with Brian. It was a phenomenal time. Brian, a true obsessive, turned the full heat of his concentration on our relationship—I rarely went to work—we spent our days and nights together and he taught me how to use the printing presses, how to develop pictures, what Carl Andre's bricks really were all about and a whole new language that gradually became less opaque and then fascinating to me. We went to galleries, exhibitions, concerts, lectures; he talked about English folk music, magic and witchcraft, fell walking, fashion, architecture, new poetry, electronic music, carpentry, cooking and a million other passions.; itinerant artists appeared and disappeared around the dinner table and stayed sometimes for days. Brian cooked and held court for changing shifts of people and we ate and drank, made love and laughed ourselves into every new day.

At this time, Brian was still involved with Simon Cutts and Kay Roberts in the Coracle Press gallery—directly opposite the flat—although I think their association was less active than it had been and Brian was ploughing more of his own furrow. Using the wonderful Adana small presses, he circulated artists' and poets' new work (including his own) to a mailing list around the world—and in return practically every post brought reciprocal work—often from countries with restrictive regimes where clandestine printing by potato die-cut or crude blocking were their only choices for making work. Brian's constant contact was a lifeline to those locked into cultural solitary confinement. And more sophisticated mail art came and went from all over the world. There were also the monolithic works that Brian was so drawn to. One involved a rubber stamp of a single puff of cannon smoke—which was to be impressed on sheets of hand-made paper once for every casualty of a battle in the Great War—it involved millions of stampings. Brian then planned to bind the pages (he was a wonderful bookbinder) and find a room in which they could be permanently stored—a moving memorial and one which reflected Brian's endless fascination with death and the rituals of mourning.

The months melted away—we never got round to marketing the 'Black Circus' catalogue—and then reality caught up and Brian announced that he was close to bankruptcy and desperate measures were called for. For some years, he had supplemented his own work by earning large sums of money as a proof reader/copy editor for the United Nations in Geneva. It was clear that a Geneva moment was now upon him but at the height of our mutual infatuation, it was unthinkable that we should be apart—he had a better plan. The Camberwell flat with its outside loo, bath in the kitchen, rotting roof and Squeeker the rat who terrorised us from the junk shop stairs, had begun to pall and Brian decided that we would give up the flat and go to Vienna together for 18 months to work for the UN. There we could save enough money to buy our own place in the English countryside and be free to work as we wished.

We started to pack Brian's life up in boxes wrapped in black plastic and numbered from one to something in the 400's—books, artworks, collections, work in progress, printing presses, witches cabinets, beloved kitchen utensils, and on and on it went—to be stored in the basement of the gallery opposite. It was enormously painful for him to see all his 'toys' (his expression) gradually disappear and the base where so much work had been accomplished and so many ideas had been bounced from wall to wall, become again a sad old tumble down S.E. London slum flat.

In retrospect this was a defining time in Brian's life—as his 'toys' disappeared, Brian's insecurities started to manifest themselves to me in the first of the black mood-changes that were to bedevil the rest of our lives together and to drive him even deeper into the alcohol poison that eventually took his life so prematurely.

The Vienna years produced a few BL works—one based on holy water from the city's many Catholic churches and the Danube, another called *Tales from the Vienna Woods* and some inspired by the wonderful Viennese Central Cemetery—final home of so many great icons of their age. But working full time for the UN at a job which was both boring and needful of intense concentration, caused Brian enormous stress. We worked on flexi-time and most days Brian would be at his desk at the UN at 5.30 or 6am to 'buy' the afternoon off for his own work.

There were two main projects that emerged—the 'Black Circus' and the beginning of 'The Murder Club'. The 'Black Circus' was a stylish, imaginative fore-runner of the multi-media 'experiences' that are now fairly commonplace. It combined old fashioned fairground peep show, theatrical illusion and state-of-the-art technology and it sought to intrigue, educate and terrify all those interested in the darker side of the human experience. It was great and before its time and, in my mundane way, I worried that no-one would back it to the number of noughts it needed to get off the ground. I was wrong and later—when we'd returned to the UK, I quite easily found an interested potential backer for the project (at Windsor Great Park) but by this time Brian had lost interest in it and we never followed up.

'The Murder Club' was an extension of the original 'Dr. Death' idea—an international club for people fascinated by death and destruction, murder and mayhem who would exchange information and collections—and to whom Brian could market his unique brand of impeccable customised ephemera, books, pamphlets, artworks and knowledge. It was another idea waiting for its time and, for the *Internet* to happen! But, even, so we got it off the ground. I clearly recollect sitting in my glass tower office on the 24th floor of the UN building writing faction stories on Crippen and George Joseph Smith and others, planning a booklet on the Virgin Martyrs and tabulating charts on capital punishment around the world. UN work rarely interrupted. 'The Murder Club' was launched and ran for some years but, more importantly, it led to *The Murder Club Guides*—successful commercially published books—and from there to the many true-crime books that were to metamorphose Brian from a working artist into an established author and an acclaimed 'murderologist' (a term I coined for him for an early book-jacket biography)—something of which he was enormously proud.

When eventually Brian and I split up—in London in the '90s, we became extremely close friends. He moved to a sagging suite of offices at the bottom of the hill on which I still live. There he ended up living and dying. I would pass his building at least twice a day and always automatically looked up to see if his light was on and whether he was working again long into the solitary night—and I'd worry about him. It's over eighteen months now since he died and the office block is boarded up, empty and condemned—but I still look up for his light every time I pass—and wish he was still there.

BELA CUNHA

THE MURDEROLOGIST

By all accounts Brian always had a fascination with death. His change of direction from art to the examination of the circumstances of murder and the exploration of the mind of murderers began with the setting up of the Murder Club and a series of six *Murder Club Guides* to various regions of Britain published in 1988–89:

1. *London*
2. *South-East England*
3. *North-West England*
4. *The Midlands*
5. *Eastern and Home Counties*
6. *South-West England and Wales*

Two further volumes were planned, but never published: North-East England and Scotland.

In 1991 came *The Butchers*, a casebook of macabre crimes and forensic detection, which would become one of Brian's most successful books and which established him as an authority in true crime writing.

Murder Update was another 1991 title, as was *The Murder Guide*. Then came the first of two encyclopaedias written in collaboration with W. Gregg, *The Encyclopaedia of Serial Killers*, in 1992, with a new, updated edition in 1996, *The New Encyclopaedia of Serial Killers*.

I remember, as clearly as if it were yesterday, the first time I spoke to Brian on the phone. Headline, his publishers (for whom I was a freelance editor), were at their wits' end. Brian had just irascibly disposed of another editor and they didn't know who to put in the firing line for his next book, *The Encyclopaedia of Forensic Science*. Being aware that I had an interest in true crime, they approached me, tentatively wondering whether I would be prepared to take this unreasonable author on. Quaking in my shoes—I have to admit—I agreed. And after that first phone conversation, I just could not equate the courteous, considerate gentleman on the other end of the line with the unreasonable ranting bully I had been told to expect. Of course, unsolved murders have always fascinated me and I eagerly quizzed Brian on his opinion about such famous ones as the Little Gregory case, the Omar Raddad conviction, which we both believed to be a miscarriage of justice, and, closer to home, the case of Dr Jones and the five-bar gate. For Brian, I think it was just a relief to finally have an editor who was interested in his subject.

After that very successful first collaboration, several other books followed:

> The Encyclopaedia of Cruel and Unusual Punishment
> The Murder Yearbook: 1993 Edition
> The Murder Yearbook: 1994 Edition
> The Murder Yearbook: 1995 Edition
> Chronicle of Twentieth-Century Murder
> The Encyclopaedia of Women Killers
> The Encyclopaedia of Mass Murder (with W. Gregg)
> The Encyclopaedia of Occult and Supernatural Murder
> The Murder Book of Days
> The Encyclopaedia of Occult, Paranormal and Magick Practices
> Killer Cults
> Crime and Detection.

Several of Brian's books became Book Club choices and his works also sold well in America. He had a big following in Japan, too. There were Japanese editions of two of his titles and more had been planned, as was a Russian edition of *The Encyclopaedia of Serial Killers*.

Working with Brian I grew to admire his professionalism, the breadth of his knowledge, the depth of his research. Brian always did things well—he was a perfectionist. He could never spell 'weird' or 'siege', though, and I teased him mercilessly, but he always took my ribbing in good part. We worked comfortably, easily together; we were a great team.

I also remember, as clearly as if it were yesterday, the day we finally met when he came to lunch at my home. It was summer and I cooked a very simple poached salmon with new potatoes and a salad. No pudding because I already knew he did not care for sweets. Food would later become very important in our relationship. We both loved preparing meals for each other and enjoyed eating each other's cooking. I remember one birthday we celebrated with a picnic in Gunnersbury Park, which consisted solely of Brian's delicious sausage rolls, a Mister Blobby cake he'd baked as a concession to my sweet tooth, and a bottle of champagne.

From that day he came to lunch and did not leave till eleven o'clock at night, the die was cast. I was entranced, bewitched by this intelligent, charming, witty, complex man, who seemed to know about every subject under the sun. I learned so much from him over the years, especially about art. And he took great delight in introducing me to new experiences. I remember his happy smile on one of our visits to the Royal Academy when he saw my immediate attraction and enthusiasm for Jackson Pollock's bold canvases.

From that first summer's day, Brian took my hand and carried me on a roller-coaster ride of emotions from which there was no getting off.

Brian lived life to the full, at a hundred miles an hour; there were never any half measures. Those of us who were lucky enough to share a part of his multi-faceted life will never forget him. For me, his sudden death left behind an emptiness that nothing can fill.

I will always miss him.

ABRIEFCHRONOLOGYOFTHELIFE
ANDWORKOFBRIANLANE

16 August 1942
Brian Peter Lane born at St. Albans.

1953–1958
Secondary education at Dame Alice Owen Grammar School, London.

1958–1963
Apprentice proof reader with Cornwall Press, London.

1959–1963
Student at London College of Printing and Graphic Design, (Diploma).

1963–1966
Worked for three commercial printers in London on full range of printing jobs.

1966–1968
Gallery Number Ten, Blackheath, London: with Maurene Sandoe (married 1965) developed gallery as one of the first contemporary artist-run spaces with associated publications often playing an integral part; there, and in other locations, organized programme of Concrete Poetry, Fluxus, performances and new music; many contacts with avant garde artists overseas.

1967
'Project 67': name for new literary-graphic project and imprint of Gallery's publications.

1968–1969
Experimental music / avant-garde performances under title of 'Rainbow Day, Brian Lane and the First Dream Machine' with 'Rainbow Day' (Mary) as constant working companion.

1969
United Nations, Geneva, proof-reader and sub-editor.

1969–1970
Gallery Number Ten, (also new events / performances with Maurene Sandoe); produced new range of publications under imprint of 'Probable Latitude 76° 15' Longitude 113° 10'E' until closure of gallery, for financial reasons, in late-1970.

1970–1971
'Probable Latitude ...' publications now distributed by Maurene Sandoe from 'Gemma Three', Welling, Kent; also some new titles published under Gemma Three imprint.

1970–1973
Black Circus Designs Ltd, London, graphic designer and print consultant.

1973–1974
International Telecommunications Union, Geneva; proof reader and copy preparer.

1974–1975
Science Museum, London: worked in Publications Section and in Press and Public Relations Department.

1974–1977
Long-term collaboration with the artist Michael Lumb (as 'Lumb Lane'), dissolved during final stages of work on 'Catalogue' planned as culmination of project; (some of the works / projects subsequently published under their own names).

1975–1976
Acted as Technical Advisor during initial phase of Coracle Press, London.

1976
Met Debbie Squires (married 1979), who later collaborated on a number of projects.

1976–1978
International Telecommunications Union, Geneva (as previously); also used location for new projects (often in the format of index card files).

1979–1980
Post Office, London, "to satisfy the requirements of a mortgage application".

1978–1982
Worked with Simon Cutts on Coracle Press publications; alongside this resumed own publishing activities under new imprint: 'Editions Brian Lane', 162 Wyndham Road, London, publishing mostly his own titles, but also collaborated with other artists (catalogue: 'Brian Lane: Printed Works 1978' Jan.1979; new titles until c.1981). In 1979/80 re-made some publications from Gallery Number Ten of 1969/70. Resumed and developed extensive contacts with mail artists in other countries, especially Eastern Europe.

1980–
'Doctor Death, Ice White and the Black Circus': edited and produced large range of associated publications and merchandise; extensive illustrated catalogue, 1981; incorporated as a Limited Company, 1984.

1981
Met Susan Dunkley.

1982–1984
United Nations, Vienna, proof reader / copy preparer; own projects now include photographic studies of Vienna cemeteries.

1984–1985
Resumed working with Coracle Press.

1985
Ran Coracle's bookshop at Whitechapel Art Gallery (with John Bevis and Ian Farr).

1986
Edited catalogue for 'The Artist Publisher', with Simon Cutts; exhibition organized by Coracle Press for the Crafts Council, London.

1985
Founded 'The Murder Club' and began work on long series of 'Murder Club Guides'.

1985–
As 'true crime' writer and self-styled 'murderologist' published many popular paperbacks on crime, punishment and mystery; made regular appearances on radio and TV with a weekly television programme broadcast by Central Television.

1993
Met Bela Cunha.

1995
'Danse Macabre' productions launched from 7 Belmont Hill, London SE13, with its own range of publications 'as part of its historic broadsheets project'.

25 October 1999
Died from heart attack after recovery from serious illness in previous year.

NOTES ON THE CONTRIBUTORS

John Bevis Writer and editor. Worked with Coracle Press throughout the 1980s on projects including 'The Artist Publisher', The Whitechapel Bookshop, and *The Unpainted Landscape*. His seminal book *An A–Z of Birdsong* was published in 1995.

Bela Cunha Editor of murderology and allied material; partner of Brian Lane during this phase of his work.

Simon Cutts Poet, and editor, with Erica van Horn, of Coracle Press.

Susan Dunkley Partner of Brian Lane for thirteen years during the 1980s and 90s, seeing his transition from working artist to successful commercial writer. After many years as Arts Sponsorship Manager for Channel 4 is planning to re-locate to the Sussex Coast.

Adrian Glew Curator at the Tate Gallery Archive, London from 1985, and has long been aware of Brian Lane's importance in Fluxus circles.

Bill Harpe Founder and co-ordinator of The Blackie (Great Georges) Community Cultural Project in Liverpool, and has been much involved in Performance work.

John Janssen Collector, Bibliographer, & Statistician.

Michael Lumb Artist and teacher, collaborating with Brian Lane as 'Lumb Lane' during the 1970s on numerous projects, in particular, landscape works and performances in Suffolk. Currently preparing an exhibition of the work of Brian Lane.

Colin Sackett Artist, book designer and writer.

Hugh Shrapnel Composer, studied with Norman Demuth and Cornelius Cardew 1966–69, and subsequently became member of the Scratch Orchestra and other experimental music groups. Collaborated with Brian Lane on projects in the early 1970s including *Opera* and the Lorca Event in Liverpool.

Mo Tingey As Maurene Sandoe, worked extensively with Brian Lane, whom she had married in 1965. With BL, set up Gallery Number Ten, and subsequently published work under the imprint Gemma Three.

Steve Wheatley Artist, Lecturer, and editor of White Lies Publications. From the mid-1970s worked with Brian Lane on joint publications and collaborated on early Murder Club material.

Research Group for Artists Publications

Formed by Martin Rogers in 1994 at the School of Art and Design, University of Derby. RGAP comprises a core group of artists / researchers based at Derby, together with a number of external associates, advisors and professionals in the field.

RGAP publishes artists' books / publications / editions / multiples, and works with other centres in the UK and abroad, setting up collaborative projects, publications, exhibitions and conferences. In addition, it seeks to promote and facilitate research, discussion, and debate.

RGAP has published editions by composers, writers, sound and performance artists, as well as visual artists, and works have been featured in numerous exhibitions related to artists' books and publications.

RGAP is supported by the University of Derby.